Sally Rockwell, Nutritionist
presents

1413 STATE STREET
MERTZTOWN, PA 19539 - 8943
610 - 682 - 2104   800 - 733 - 4065

D0779957

TASTY - LOW CARBOHYDRATE RECIPES AND MENU PLANS

A simple handbook on how to recognize and control problems caused by yeast over-growth.

- DESCRIBES SYMPTOMS (see quiz)

- OFFERS SOLUTIONS
  Treat with anti-fungals
  Replant good bacteria
  Stop feeding the yeast
  READ COPING WITH CANDIDA

NUTRITIONIST CREATES
SELF HELP COPE & COOK SERIES FOR ALLERGIES & CANDIDA CONTROL.
TOTALLY FREE OF ALL **GRAINS, EGGS, MILKS, SOY, YEAST & REFINED SUGARS.**

Sally Rockwell
P.O. Box 31065
Seattle, Washington 98103 USA
Telephone (206) 547-1814

Coping with Candida Cookbook

ISBN 0-916575-00-4

Hang in there - you will get well. ♡ *Sally*

Send for sample newsletter! *see p. 176.* ♡ *Sally*

SICK AND TIRED of feeling SICK AND TIRED'??

BEGINNING TO WONDER IF IT IS ALL IN YOUR MIND?

iii

(on page 184)

ABOUT THE AUTHOR

"IS THERE LIFE AFTER ALLERGIES?"

Sally has gone beyond her degree in nutrition to study a wide variety of approaches to good health. Her personal victory over a history of addictions, allergies and hypoglycemia inspired the desire to help others.

Sally Rockwell
B.S. in Nutrition, University of Washington

A colorful past and a quick wit make her a frequent guest on local and national radio and T.V. talk shows. She travels far and wide lecturing and conducting workshops to put some fun into meal planning.

YES, THERE'S LIFE AFTER ALLERGIES

AFFILIATIONS:

Professional development includes: Society of Clinical Ecology; Huxley Institute; Canadian Schizophrenic Foundation; N.W. and International Academys of Preventive Medicine; Intn'l College of Applied Nutrition; Preventive Dentistry; J.B. College of Naturopathic Medicine; and others.

SELF-HELP RESOURCES

- ALLERGY ALERT NEWSLETTER Monthly updates.
- COPING WITH CANDIDA COOKBOOK Yeast overgrowth.
- THE ROTATION GAME The Survival Kit for Food Allergies.
- ROTATED ALLERGY RECIPES

PLUS

Workshops; Cooking Classes; Individual Counseling; Lectures and Support Groups (F.A.S.T. - Food Allergy Support Teams).

CONTENTS

Introduction: What is Candida 1
  Steps for Control 2
Dietary Guidelines 4
Master Chart.......................7
Cave Man Diet 9
Don't Feed the Yeast...............11
Questions and Answers 12
Counting Carbohydrates 15
Foods to Avoid 17
Live it up Foods and Snacks 18
Caution! High Carbos 21
Carbohydrate Listings 22
Ideal vs. Real Diets 35
Fast Food Eateries 36
How to Clean Foods 38
Social Occasions 40
Dining Out 41
Breakfast Ideas 42
Lunch Ideas 43
Dinner Ideas.......................44
Brown Bag Lunches, Traveling 46
Sandwich Fillings 48
Spreads and Dips 49

How to Sprout Sprouts 51
Sprouting Guide 52

RECIPES
Curried Lentils 54
Savory Beans 55
Blushed Cauliflower 56
Spiced Eggplant 57
Marinated Vegetables 58
Sophisticated Vegetables 60
Crab Bisque 61
Sesame Vegetables 61
Beansprout Hot Dish. 62
Green Beans & Burger 63
Neapolitan Zucchini 64
Basic Salad Dressing 67
Green Goddess Dressing 67
French Dressing 68
Guacamole 68
Zesty BBQ Sauce 69
Ketchup 69
Gado Gado Sauce 70
Clam Sauce/Clam Soup 71

CONTENTS

Nut and Seed butters and Milks 73
Tasty Toppings 72
Seasoned Salt 72
Almond Soup 75
Clam & Avocado Broth 75
Beet Borscht 76
Broccoli Soup 77
Garlic Soup 78
Hot & Sour Soup 79
Peasant Vegetable Soup 80
Minestrone 81
Onion Soup 82
Seafood Boullion 83
Spinach Soup 84
Zucchini Soup 84
Turkey Vegetable Soup 85

SALADS
Avocado Mousse 87
Chinese Salad 87
Crabmeat & Avocado 88
Bean Sprout Salad 89
Spinach Salad 90

Sesame Cucumber Salad 90
Fish Salad 91
Gala Salad 92
Hearty Salad 93
Seafood Salad 94
Russian Salad I 95
Russian Salad II 95
Shrimp W/Lemon Dill 96
Taboulie Salad 97
Stuffed Tomatoes 98
Turkey Salad 99
Tofuna 100

MAIN DISHES
Hearty Hash (hurry up) 103
Falafel 104
Sunflower Wedge 105
 Veggie Nut Loaf 105
Sunflower Carrot Casserole 106
Nut Loaf 107
Ponset 108
Meat Roast Guide 110
Pot Roast 113

CONTENTS

Waistline Beef Patties 114
Veal a la mode 115
Poultry Roasting Guide 117
Almond Rabbit 118
Lemon Broiled Chicken 119
Chicken & Broccoli Bake 120
Sesame Chicken 121
Chicken Stroganoff 122
Curried Turkey Thighs 123
Summer Garden Turkey 124
Mexican Turkey 125
Korean Broiled Steak 126
Fish types, Cooking Hints 127
Guide to Cooking Fish 129
Fillet Almandine 131
Herbed Baked Fish 132
Baked Stuffed Fish 133
Fillet in Italian Sauce 134
Mahi Mahi Lyonnaise 135
Stuffed Turbot 136
Tuna Casserole 136
Boiled Prawns 137
Broiled Shellfish 138

Bouillabaisse 139
Hearty Alaska Chowder 140
Clams & Amaranth 141
New Orleans Gumbo 142
Fish with Shrimp Sauce 143
Seafood Ragout 144
Sauteed Scallops 145
Scallops St. Jacques 146
Shellfish Cocktail 147
Slow (Crock Pot) Cooking 149
Basic Beans - how to cook 150
Basic Grain Cooking 151
Amaranth and Quinoa..............152
Coatings for Baked and Fried 153
Vinegar Substitutes 153
Flour Substitutes 155
Helpful Cooking Measures 157
Egg Substitutes 158
Thickeners, Binders, and Gums....159
Leavenings, Baking Powder 160

CONTENTS

Cheat Section

Crackers & Pie Crusts.............161
Nutri Ola (Granola) 163
Basic Muffins 165
Basic Pancakes & Waffles (flour) .167
Sesame Pancakes 168
Beancakes 169
Frozen Cranberry Salad 171
Fruit & Seed Bars 171
Pumpkin Bread 172
Rum Balls 173
Nut Butter Fudge Candy 173
Rotation Game....................174
Allergy Recipes Book.............175
Cassette Tapes...................176
Ordering information.............177
Index 179

SEE CANDIDA QUIZ---page 184

WHAT IS CANDIDA ? ? ?

Candida Albicans is the name of a yeast. Yeasts are in the same family as molds, mildews and fungus; just like "Golden Delicious" is the name of an apple in the fruit family. Yeasts and bacterias are in different families, or categories, just as fruits and vegetables are in different categories.

Friendly and unfriendly germs live everywhere, including in and on our bodies. Our intestines are full of friendly bacteria who work for us by helping to digest foods, produce vitamins and so on. A few yeast hang around also, they don't seem to do work for us, but they don't harm us either, for the good bacteria won't let the yeast grow into colonies large enough to cause problems.

Antibiotics kill bacteria, both the good and bad bacteria, but they don't kill yeast. The past abuse of prescribing antibiotics for any and everything that had to do with illness, plus the huge amounts in our food supply, are causing the bacteria to die out. This gave the yeast (who haven't had room to grow before) a chance to overgrow and fill our intestines so that the good bacteria gets crowded out.

Candida yeast spits out toxins (poisons) that our bodies have to deal with and that's what is making us sick and is also weakening our immune systems. Birth control pills, steroids (cortisone type drugs), even pregnancy interferes with hormonal balance and encourages undesireable yeast overgrowth.

We need to rebalance our systems in order to break this downward, self perpetua -ting cycle and start rebuilding our health.

1

WELCOME --- LET'S HAVE FUN ON OUR "JOURNEY TO WELLNESS" .

FOUR MAIN STEPS OF TREATMENT   (Do all four at the same time):

1. Exterminate the Yeast
Antifungals (yeast killers) such as nystatin, nyzoral (see your physician); or
Pau d'arco (also called La Pacho or Ipe Roxo) tea or extract; garlic.
Of the various types of garlic available, fresh is always best. If not socially
acceptable then choose an odorless product.

An odorless, readily digestible liquid, KYOLIC, is organic, free of chemicals,
and easily digested. Available in health food stores or contact:
Waukanaga of America   23510 Telo Ave. #5   Torrance, CA. 90505
A convenient tablet form in a lemon/parsley base is distributed by Miller Pharm.
245 West Roosevelt Road, Post Office Box 279S W., Chicago, Ill. 60185.

Doctors using homeopathic remedies are experiencing positive results also.
See page four to get on-going, up-to-date Candida resources and information.

2. Replace the Good Bacteria
L. Acidophilus is the name of the bacteria that belongs in our gut (also known
as large intestine or lower bowel). It is the same bacteria (germ) that turns
milk into yogurt. If we take acidophilus to replace the good bacteria at the
same time we take antibiotics, the yeast wouldn't have room to grow. A milk-free
powder is Vitaldophilus or Primedophilus by Klaire Labs, Box 618 Carlsbad, CA.
92008.

3. Rebuild the Immune System

Rebuild the immune system with fish oils such as MaxEpa, or Evening Primrose Oil, linseed oil, cold pressed sunflower or safflower oil. (Current studies suggest that we get enough of these oils, but just don't digest or absorb them.) Do take an allergy-free vitamin & mineral supplement, plus extra B complex & C.

4. Starve Out the Yeast

See the "Don't Feed The Yeast" section. According to Dr. J. Rippon, expert on fungus, the yeast feed on all sugars and fruits and nuts and they don't feed on other yeasts or alcohol. Apparently their growth is stimulated by certain hormones, also. (See PMS discussion, page 14.)

Ideally, starches (carbohydrates) are broken down into simple sugars and digested and/or absorbed in our small intestines. If our digestion is poor, and we have food allergies, then the sugars provide nourishment for the yeast. Who knows if what occurs in a laboratory test tube happens the same way in our guts. Do they add digestive enzymes and hydrochloric acid (stomach acid) to test tubes? Do our stressed bodies produce ample digestive juices?

My experience is that any starch in quantity may cause adverse reactions, ESPECIALLY GRAINS. Nuts are OK if we chew them (most of us don't chew our food well enough). Can't tolerate nuts? Perhaps it's the mold on them. Try roasting them for five minutes at 300 degrees F.

THIS IS NOT TO BE TAKEN AS MEDICAL ADVICE, it is information only. See a physician who understands this dilemma.

Research on Candida, allergies & the immune system is literally exploding in every direction. Keep up-to-date on the latest findings with my ALLERGY ALERT andCANDIDA UPDATE. For information on new techniques and products that seem to help, see page eight.

Coping with Candida is a friendly guide to help you cope with the yeast problem and to rid yourself of the critters by following a low carbohydrate menu plan. No carbohydrates for one month or more seems to work best, then gradually increase up to, but not exceeding 80 grams per day, for adults. **Do not** restrict children's intake of carbohydrates for they need the energy for growth and activity, just restrict the **type** of starches (no refined sugars of any kind).

Those who don't tolerate nystatin or other anti-fungals may be able to take it after a week on a no carbohydrate diet, which seems to diminish the yeast colonies and make the drug more effective and more tolerable.

Prepare side dishes of whole grains and starchy vegetables for the kids. Adults need to stick to simple proteins, some beans and peas and lots of vegetables.

The Carbohydrate count of all foods we normally eat is included for you to keep track of your intake. It is not "O.K." to eat all the foods found on the list. Sugars and starches are also listed for your information so that you can see what a feast you provide for the hungry yeast when you indulge in too many starches.

A cookbook is a guide, not a straight jacket. Lighten up-get creative--use your imagination!

I've corrected all the mistakes that occured in the original <u>COPING</u> <u>WITH</u> <u>CANDIDA</u> and now this NEW, REVISED EDITION will probably exhibit some more. My expert proof-reader (Dani) and I have done our best to catch them all.

(≠ LISA)

ATTENTION ALL PERFECTIONISTS! I know you won't judge the contents of this book or my expertise as a nutritionist and a scholar upon my typing skills. If you find a mistake, please let me know. I'll correct the next edition. THANK YOU.

Remember that the Goal of this therapeutic diet is to STARVE OUT THE YEAST so you can IMPROVE YOUR HEALTH, it's not forever, just until the symptoms subside and the immune system has a chance to rest and rebuild. A healthy body will not allow yeast to take over, nor dis-ease to overwhelm us either.

As a nutritionist I want to concentrate on helping you with menu plans and ideas for coping with cooking. Hopefully this too-brief explanation of candida yeast will furnish you with just enough background to help you understand WHY we need to avoid sugars and "allergenic" types of foods.

We need to be on a low carbo diet for from 3 months to 3 years. The more strictly we follow the diet at first, the sooner we'll be rid of the critters.

A low-carbohydrate diet does NOT have to be a high-protein diet!!

Replace the grain and fruit with four times as many vegetables as you've eaten in the past. Indulge in huge amounts of soups, salads, and steamed vegies.

After the first month of this low-carbohydrate diet, please start rotating your foods. Repetitive eating, eating the same foods day after day after day is a major cause of food allergies. The rotation diet can help rebuild a weakened immune system and reduce stress so we can get healthy and energetic.

The abbreviated form of the Master Chart from my Rotation Game will get you started with the idea of rotation, eating a food only once every four days. I've omitted the foods to omit while on the Candida program, so, what you see is what you get.

Day 1 is GREEN DAY; day 2 is YELLOW DAY; day 3 is BLUE DAY; day 4 is RED DAY. The simple color coding system is explained in my ROTATION GAME. See page 174 for more information on the game's FUN, EASY-TO-USE color coding system.

The accompanying book, Sally Rockwell's Allergy Recipes has color-coded pages that coincide with the colors on the MASTER CHART of the ROTATION GAME. The GAME and RECIPE BOOK deal with rotating foods and surviving without gluten, (or any grains), refined sugars, milk, yeast, soy or any other problem foods.

As an ex junk-food-junkie, I like to eat yummy food and I don't like feeling deprived. I gave up sugars, coffee, cigarettes, alcohol, amphetamines and tranquilizers in 1975. I haven't had any grains or milk products for about eight years and so I was inspired to develop tasty, easy-to-fix, allergy-free recipes. for myself and for others with the same dilemma.

P.O. BOX 31065
SEATTLE, WA 98103
(206) 547-1814

the rotation game →

A DIVERSIFIED ROTATION MENU PLAN
MASTER CHART   PLAN I

© 1981 Sally J. Rockwell

FOOD FAMILY	DAY 1	DAY 2	DAY 3	DAY 4
FISH FIN	FISH MAY BE EATEN DAILY AS LONG AS A DIFFERENT FISH IS SELECTED EACH DAY! (SEE INSTRUCTIONS)*			
SHELL	MUSSEL. ESCARGOT. CLAM	SHRIMP. LOBSTER	OYSTERS. SCALLOPS. ABALONE	CRAB. SQUID. OCTOPUS
FOWL &	CHICKEN & EGGS. GOOSE & EGGS	TURKEY & EGGS ↔	CORNISH GAME HEN. QUAIL EGGS. PHEASANT	DUCK & EGGS ↔
MEAT*	BEEF (VEAL. LIVER. ETC.)		PORK (HAM. BACON. ETC.) LAMB	RABBIT ↔
DAIRY*				
LEGUMES	KIDNEY. SOY. & LIMA BEANS		PINTO. GARBANZO & BLACK BEANS. BLACK-EYED & SPLIT PEAS	
SPROUTS	NUTS. SEEDS. LEGUMES	NUTS. SEEDS	NUTS. SEEDS. LEGUMES	NUTS. SEEDS
NUTS SEEDS & OILS*	SOY. WALNUTS. FILBERT ↔ SESAME ↔	ALMOND. PINE NUTS ↔ BRAZIL NUTS ↔ SUNFLOWER. APRICOT	PECANS. CHESTNUTS. ↔ MACADAMIA NUTS ↔ PUMPKIN OLIVE ↔	CASHEW NUTS. PISTACHIO NUTS SAFFLOWER. CORN AVOCADO ↔
	BEETS. SWISS CHARD		SPINACH	AVOCADO ↔ PARSNIP. CELERY
MUSTARD*	CABBAGE. BROCCOLI. WHITE RADISH KALE. NAPPA	CARROTS. PARSLEY	BOK CHOY. RED RADISH. BRUSSEL SPROUTS. CAULIFLOWER	
COMPOS		LEAF & BIB LETTUCE. COMMON ARTICHOKE		ICEBERG LETTUCE. ROMAINE
GOURD*	CUCUMBER. WINTER SQUASH		SUMMER SQUASH PUMPKIN. ZUCCHINI	
LILY*	ONION. GARLIC		CHIVES. LEEKS. SHALLOTS. ASPARAGUS	
NIGHT SH		WHITE POTATO. PEPPERS		TOMATO. EGGPLANT. PEPPERS
MISC.	STRING BEANS	YAMS ↔ JICAMA ↔	PEAS OKRA. OLIVE ↔ CHESTNUTS ↔	BAMBOO SHOOTS JER. ARTICHOKE ↔ SWEET POTATO ↔
BULK	PECTIN	FLAX SEED ↔	CHIA SEED ↔	PSYLLIUM SEED ↔
ENZYMES VITAMINS	CONSULT YOUR PROFESSIONAL HEALTH ADVISOR			

*REFER TO FOOD FAMILY LISTS

PROTEIN · VEGS.

7

For more detailed product information, and the latest up-to-date findings and discoveries on Candida send for my CANDIDA UPDATE and subscribe to my ALLERGY ALERT monthly newsletter. For the CANDIDA UPDATE send $1.00 and a LARGE self-addressed-stamped-envelope. No envelope? Then send $2.00 to: Sally Rockwell Box 31065 Seattle, Wa. 98103

ALLERGY ALERT NEWSLETTER (a mere $12.00/year) is filled with my latest discoveries on getting well, new recipes and a most important of all--readers questions. Write to me so that I can keep in touch with you and your needs. I can't always answer personally, but I will answer in the newsletter with your permission. Names withheld on request, of course.

NOW I CAN COME TALK TO YOU AND YOUR FRIENDS AND HELP YOU IN AND OUT OF YOUR KITCHEN with a little electronic help, that is. Both audio and visual tapes explain the whys and why nots of the diet, offer helpful hints and suggestions and answer the little, aggravating problems that accompany special diets and menu planning. Change is difficult at best, and when you don't feel good it may seem nearly impossible. **ORDER FORMS for all of the above are in the back of the book.**

Additional resources available for more in depth yeastinformation:

The Missing Diagnosis   The Yeast Connection
Dr. O. Truss   Dr. Wm. Crook
P.O. Box 26508-S   P.O. Box 3494-S
Birmingham, Al 35226   Jackson, Tenn 38303
$25.00 plus shipping $13.95 plus shipping

In order to "starve out the yeast", daily carbohydrate intake should be between 60 to 80 grams per day. Complete carbohydrate count food list is on page 18.

The only way some of us are going to survive and enjoy life fully is to reconstruct our eating habits, but if it's too difficult, or doesn't taste good we won't stick to the new way.

A major Goal in my life is to find a way to simplify and incorporate changes into our lifestyle easily, simply and without added stress. Sometimes the stress of the changes is more harmful to our health than the disease . . . well, let's make them Fun!! (or at least tolerable).

Candida is a major contributing factor in food allergies. So if we get rid of - or at least reduce the size of the colonies of Candida yeast, our food and chemical sensitivities will diminish.

The fewer yeast in our guts, the less toxins emitted into our systems. The toxins (poisons) overwhelm our immune systems and   it begins to attack foods & chemicals as though they were germs. The added stress of poor diet and probably vitamin and mineral deficiencies deplete our bodies ability to heal itself, and we begin to fall apart.

When our immune system weakens, the symptoms listed on the Candida Quiz begin to develop. So if you scored above a "3", do read this book. Or, at the very least try the simple "Cave Man Diet" plan for 10 days and note any changes in your mental and physical functions.

Keep a thorough record of all you eat and drink. Note aches, pains, skin rashes, itchy ears or rectum, muscle soreness, stiffness. Pay attention to positive changes in attitude, such as more patience, calmer, increased self esteem, clearer thinking, less sleep requirements, and more.

Feeling worse for the first 3 days is normal, sometimes up to 5 days, and then the old complaints should start to disappear, one at a time. I didn't know I was depressed until I wasn't; didn't know I only require 6 maybe 7 hours of sleep instead of 9 plus; I think I'm a teenager (feel like one) until the mirror reminds me I'm not, (darn).

CAVE MAN DIET

Lots and lots and lots of vegetables:
Raw is best, of course, then steamed, then stir fried. See page 7 for ideas, because we forget what's available besides carrot sticks, celery and lettuce.

Lots of protein foods:
Fish, shellfish, chicken, turkey, rabbit, (again, see page 7.) nuts and seeds.

Absolutely Avoid:
Sugars of any type, fruit, breads or pastas, milk products or yeasty-fermented foods. [Do not restrict children's starches, just sugars (see page 4)] You will get well faster if you avoid all grains at first. If you are allergic to a grain and don't know it, and it may keep you in a depressed state. You may not experience the rush of clarity and exuberance one usually feels after getting off all the toxic foods. Foods that were causing us to feel dull, depressed and out of sorts.

One of the reasons yeast overgrowth occurs is because they are so well fed by our 'typical American diet' high in sugars and refined starches (white flour, white rice, white noodles, etc.). The yeast thrive on all types of sugars, even the more wholesome ones such as honey and date sugar. All sugars, even fruits and whole grains are a hearty meal for the hungry yeast.

Q. Do Vinegars and other "Yeasty" Foods Feed the Yeast?

A. No, they don't feed the yeast. But we are very likely to be allergic to yeast for it is thriving in our bodies. By eating and being exposed to molds, yeasts, mildews and fungus (all relatives of the candida yeast), we stress our immune system and place an extra load on our already over burdened body. (See the 'avoid' list page 17 for foods in this category.)

Q. Can We Use Fructose or Barley Malt or Molasses?

A. NO!! All types of sweeteners (except artificial) are tabu. I do not recommend artificial sweeteners. However, during 'transitional diets' (kicking the sugar habit) or therapeutic diets like this one we need all the help we can get, and they help ease the transition from sweet to less sweet and finally to unsweetened dishes.

Q. Are Potatoes and Starchy Vegetables O.K.?

A. Yes, in small amounts. Eat the starchy foods in small quantities throughout the day, not all at once so that you don't feed the yeast. Restrict carbohydrates to 60 to 80 grams per day.

Q. HOW LONG DO I HAVE TO STAY ON THIS DIET?

A. Anywhere from 3 months to 3 years, depending on the severity of the infestation, how closely you stay on the diet; how often you "cheat"; how long you've had the overgrowth, your everyday stress levels; the type of antifungal used and how soon the 'good' bacteria (acidophilus) get replanted in the intestine.

Q. What About Kids, Don't They Need Starches?

A. Yes, growing kids need starches. So restrict the type of starch, not the quantity. Refined sugars and fruit juices are a no-no. Limit fruits (especially fruit juices), and grains to small quantities . Stay away from cow's milk and wheat for a while. Goat's milk may be OK. Beans, peas and starchy vegetables are O.K. (See the food lists).

Q. What If I Cheat

A.   Eating sweets feeds the yeast and allows them to multiply quite rapidly. The more yeast in your gut, the more toxins (poisons) released into your system which bring on the old symptoms and depression.

Q. How Harmful Is Cheating?

A. Almost all of us go off the diet occasionally, just get back on it the very next day. What's harmful is playing 'kick me' and 'poor me' and telling yourself you're a bad person for slipping off.

Q. <u>How</u> <u>Far</u> <u>Can</u> <u>I</u> <u>Go</u> <u>Off</u> <u>the</u> <u>Diet</u> without <u>Destroying</u> <u>All</u> <u>the</u> <u>Good</u> <u>I've</u> <u>Done?</u>

A. I don't know if anyone knows that, but you'll find out just how far you can go after slipping once or twice. Take your Buffered Vitamin C powder; Alka-Seltzer (gold label, only) or baking soda and then get back on the diet IMMEDIATELY.

Q. <u>Is</u> <u>There</u> <u>a</u> <u>Safe</u> <u>Way</u> <u>to</u> <u>Cheat?</u>

A. Well, sort of. Try the recipes in the "cheat sections" of this book instead of eating commercial sweets full of perservatives and artificial garbage. Refined sugars tend to be addicting to most of us with allergies, which means a little bit just creates a need for more. They are the 'trigger' foods that cause us to crave more, to 'pig out' and binge until misery sets in. Unrefined sugars don't seem to be 'triggers'.

Q. <u>What</u> <u>Can</u> <u>I</u> <u>Eat</u> <u>When</u> <u>the</u> <u>Urge</u> <u>to</u> <u>Cheat</u> <u>is</u> <u>Overwhelming?</u>

A. I've devoted a section of recipes and suggestions for cheating without totally destroying yourself, to be used for <u>Emergencies</u> <u>Only.</u>

Q. <u>Why</u> <u>Do</u> <u>I</u> <u>Crave</u> <u>Sweets</u> <u>and</u> <u>Carbohydrates?</u>

A. It's a matter of survival of the fittest for most living creatures, even yeast. When they need nourishment I laughingly say they are hollering up "Feed Me, I'm Hungry". They trick you into eating sugars and starches. A colleague, Leslie Kroker, R.N., tells her patients they are in your gut "<u>banging</u> <u>their</u> <u>spoons</u> <u>for</u> <u>nourishment</u>".

13

Q. Why Not A "No Carbohydrate" Diet?

A. I recommend the CAVE MAN DIET (p.10) the first week, longer if tolerated. The yeast die off faster. Ketosis and rapid weight loss usually occur when carbohydrate intake is less than 60 grams a day. Check with your doctor.

Q. When Do I Increase My Carbohydrates?

A. When your are feeling symptom-free. slowly add fruits, then beans and peas, add grains last (see page 16). If you get gas and bloating or your old symptoms return when you increase carbohydrates then cut back again, for you are feeding the yeast.

Q. How is this Connected to "Pre-Menstral Tension (PMS)"?

A. When I had the Candida yeast overgrowth (which was most of my life) I would start pacing the floor, craving sweets about 10 days before the full moon, (even after my uterus was removed). Our ovaries signal a hormone, progesterone, to increase the sugar levels in mucous membranes, which in turn encourage yeast growth. The theory is that the growing yeast need more sugars to survive and so craving begins . . the yeast want to be fed.

Q. Why Do Other PMS Symptoms (additional to bingeing) Occur?

A. Candida yeast emits toxins into your body. That plus a hormone imbalance, vitamin and mineral deficiencies, can cause the depression, headaches, edema, etc.

HOW TO CALCULATE CARBOHYDRATE AMOUNTS IN A RECIPE

The Formula:

Total # of grams in recipe

_____   = equals the number of carbo-
                                            hydrates per serving

Divided by = # of grams per serving

Example: Crackers or Pie Crust

Made with flour   Made with nut meal

| 1 cup flour | 70 grams |
| oil | 0 grams |

| Total grams | 70 |
| # of crackers | 30 | =2.3gms each |

| 1 cup nut meal | 20 grams |
| 1/3 cup arrowroot | 10 grams |

| Total grams | 30 |
| # of crackers | 30 | =1gm each |

(All counts are approximate)

Remember, for adults stay between 60-80 grams of carbohydrates a day. DO NOT restrict children's intake, just keep them off sugars.

HOW TO ADD CARBOHYDRATES (STARCHES) BACK INTO YOUR DIET

GRADUALLY add SMALL AMOUNTS of fruits, starchy vegetables, beans and peas,
before you begin to add back the grains or cow's milk. For best results, keep a
"Food and Symptom Dairy" as described in the ROTATION GAME, pages 16 and 17.
You will be able to recognize "allergic" reactions to foods (including yeasty
foods) and separate those reactions from "feeding the yeast" symptoms that
happen from eating too many carbohydrates.

Add the foods that you've been avoiding back into your diet in the following
order whenever possible: Quinoa, amaranth, millet, buckwheat, barley, brown
rice, wild rice, oats, rye, corn and **add wheat last.** When adding dairy try
goat's milk products first: yogurt, (homemade, if possible), cheeses, then the
milk. Dried or canned goat's milk is readily available in most health food
stores. Repeat the same procedure with cow's milk.

Be prepared for withdrawal and "die-off" symptoms such as: headaches, body
aches, intense cravings, irritability, nausea, etc. Remember to take buffered
Vit C powder (start with 1/8 tsp in water between meals & gradually increase to
1/2 tsp, as tolerated) or Bi-Carbs by Klaire Labs, or Alka Seltzer- the Gold
label. Try to exercize, be good to yourself, be your own best friend. I chewed
massive amounts of sugarless gum to satisfy my cravings, I know gum is full of
undesireable chemicals but it did keep me away from eating sugars and starches
until my urges to "pig-out" left me and I finally regained my "sanity".

IN THE BEGINNING, AVOID

1. **All Sweetners**
   Sugars, honey, maple syrup, date sugar, fructose, etc.

2. **All Fruits**
   Frozen, canned or dried. SMALL amounts of fresh may be OK.*
   No frozen fruit juices (high mold and high sugar content).

3. **All Grains**
   After about two weeks begin to add starches NOT related to wheat:
   buckwheat, wild rice, amaranth and quinoa, next try barley, corn,
   oats, millet, rice, rye and finally add wheat.

4. **All Types of Yeast***
   Brewer's, Bakers, nutritional, tortula. Read the labels, yeast is used as a
   flavoring in lots of "health" foods.

5. **Fermented, Yeasty and Moldy Foods***
   Mushrooms, pickles, old cheeses, vinegar, soy sauce, beer and wine.

See page 14 for discussion on when and how to increase carbohydrates and page 10
describes the CAVE MAN DIET.

*These foods do not "Feed the Yeast", but may cause allergic reactions.

SNACKS

FOODS YOU CAN EAT FREELY.   'Live It Up List!'

Food	Portion	Approx. Grams of Carbohydrate
Almonds	1/4 cup	3
Almond Meal	1 cup	17
Brazil Nuts	1/4 cup	2
Cashews (caution)	1/4 cup	10
Cashew Meal (caution)	1 cup	50
Filberts	1/4 cup	5
Filbert Meal	1 cup	25
Hazel Nuts	10	12
Lichee Nuts	6	11
Macadamia Nuts	1/2 cup	10
Pecans	1/4 cup	4
Pine Nuts	1/2 cup	6
Pistachios	20	2
Pumpkin Seeds	1/4 cup	8
Sunflower Seeds	1/4 cup	7
Walnuts	1/4 cup	5
Almond Butter	1 tbsp	3
Cashew Butter	1 tbsp	5
Sesame Butter	1 tbsp	3
Butter		0

NOTES

18

FOODS YOU CAN EAT FREELY. 'Live It Up List!'

These vegetables contain relatively little carbohydrate.

Food	Portion	Approx. Grams of Carbohydrate
Artichokes	1 cup	10
Asparagus	1 cup	5
Bamboo Shoots	1/2 cup	4
Bean Sprouts	1 cup	5
Beets	1 cup	12
Broccoli	1 cup	7
Brussel Sprouts	1 cup	10
Cabbage	1 cup	6
Carrots	1 cup	10
Carrots	1 raw	5
Cauliflower	1 cup	5
Celery	1 cup	5
Celery	1 lg stalk	2
Cress	1 cup	10
Chard, cooked	1 cup	2
Cucumbers	1 cup	4
Eggplant	1 cup	8
Endive	2 stalks	4
Escarole	2 lg leaves	2
Fennel	2 stalks	2
Garlic	1 oz	9
Greens:		
Beet	1 cup	5
Collard	1 cup	7
Dandelion	1 cup	5
Kale	1 cup	7
Mustard	1 cup	6
Turnip	1 cup	8
Spinach, raw	1 cup	4
Spinach, cooked	1 cup	6
Kohlrabi	1 cup	10

19

FOODS YOU CAN EAT FREELY. 'Live It Up List!' (cont'd)

Food	Portion	Approx. Grams of Carbohydrate
Lambsquarter	1/2 cup	8
Leeks	3 med	8
Lettuce, all varieties	1 cup	2
Okra	1 cup	10
Onions	1 med	9
Parsley	1 cup	5
Pepper, red or green	1 med	5
Pimiento	1 med	2
Radishes	2 sm	7
Rutabega	1 cup	12
Soybeans	1 cup	10
Snowpeas (pea pods)	15	6
Sprouts	1 cup	11
String Beans	1 cup	7
Summer Squash*	1 cup	8
Tomatoes, fresh	1 cup	4
Turnips	1 cup	12

20

*Winter squash may be identified by a tough non-edible skin, where as Summer squash skin is edible.

CAUTION!! High Carbohydrate Vegetables

Caution	Portion	Approx. Grams of Carbohydrate
Corn	1/2 cup	30
Lima Beans	1/2 cup	24
English Peas	1/2 cup	20
White Potatoes	1/2 cup or 1 sm	32 to 40
Winter Squash, Acorn, Butternut or Hubbard	1/2 cup	10
Sweet Potatoes	1/2 cup	30
Beans and Peas, dried and cooked	1/2 cup	20
Lentils	1/2 cup	22
Peas, fresh, cooked	1 cup	19
Parsnips	1 cup	20
Popcorn, popped	1 cup	11
Potatoes, white	1 med	21
Potatoes, French fried	10	13
Potatoes, mashed	1/2 cup	14
Pumpkin, cooked	1 cup	18

CARBOHYDRATE LISTINGS

Food	Portion	Grams
Amaranth Flour	1 cup	62
Almonds, shelled	1/2 cup	14
Almonds, shelled	12 to 15	3
Almond Meal	1 cup	17
Anchovies, canned	8 sm	0
Apples, raw	1 med	18
Applesauce	1 cup	26
Apricots, fresh	2 to 3 med	10
Arrowroot	1 tbsp	7
Artichokes, Jerusalem	4 sm	17
Artichokes, base	1	5
Asparagus, cooked	6 stalks	4
Avocado	1/2 med	6
Bacon	1 lb.	0
Bamboo shoots, raw	3/4 cup	6
Bananas, fresh	1 med	26
Barley, dry	1 cup	120
Bass		0
Bean Sprouts, raw	1 cup	5
Beans, Green, cooked	1 cup	8
Beans, Kidney, cooked	1 cup	42
Beans, Lima, cooked	1 cup	34
Bean Flour	1 cup	63
Beef		0
Beet Greens, cooked	1 cup	6
Beets, cooked	1 cup	16
Biscuits	1 med	20
Blackberries, fresh	1 cup	18
Blueberries, fresh	1 cup	21
Bluefish, baked		0
Bouillon Cube, beef or chicken	1 cube	0

CARBOHYDRATE LISTINGS

Food	Portion	Grams
Brains, all kinds	3 oz.	1
Brazil Nuts, shelled	1/2 cup	11
Bread Crumbs, dry	1 cup	65
Breads:		
Corn	1 slice	22
Cracked Wheat	1 slice	12
Broccoli, cooked	1 cup	8
Brussels Sprouts	1 cup	12
Butter		0
Butternuts	4 or 5	1
Cabbage, shredded	1 cup	5
Cabbage, Chinese	1 cup	3
Cakes:		
Angel Food	1 slice	23
Butter, iced	1 slice	48
Carob Powder	1/2 cup	80
Cantaloupe	1/4 melon	9
Carrots, raw	1	5
Carrots, raw,		
grated	1 cup	10
Casaba Melon	1 wedge	13
Cashew Nut	1 cup	35
Cashew Nuts	6 to 8	4
Cauliflower	1 cup	6
Celery, raw	1 lg stalk	2
Celery, raw	1 cup	4
Cereals:		
Bran	1 cup	43
Corn, puffed	3/4 cup	25
Corn, flakes	1 cup	25
Cream of Wheat,		
cooked	1 cup	27
Oat, ready to eat	1 cup	18
Oat, rolled	2/3 cup	18
Oatmeal, cooked	1 cup	23

CARBOHYDRATE LISTINGS

Food	Portion	Grams
Cereals:		
Rice, puffed	1 cup	12
Rice, flakes	1 cup	27
Rice Krispies	1 cup	25
Rolled Oats, cooked	1/3 cup	19
Wheat, puffed	1 cup	10
Wheat, flakes, crushed	1 cup	56
Chard Leaves, cooked	1 cup	2
Chayote	4 oz	7
Cheese:		
American	1 oz	1
Cottage	1 cup	5
Cream	1 tbsp	0
Cherries, fresh, sour or sweet	1 cup	20
Chestnut Flour	4 oz	76
Chestnuts	2 lg	7
Chicken		0
Chicory	5 leaves	4
Chili Powder	1 tbsp	1
Chives, chopped	1 tbsp	0
Chop Suey	1/2 cup	10
Cider, sweet	1 cup	26
Clam dip, sour cream	3 tsp	1
Clams, steamers	6	5
Cocoa Powder	1 tbsp	3
Coconut, fresh	2 in. square	6
Coconut, fresh, shredded	1 cup	13
Coconut Milk	1 cup	12
Codfish		0
Cookies:		
Arrowroot	1 cookie	4
Brownies	1 brownie	16
Corn, kernels	1 cup	26

CARBOHYDRATE LISTINGS

Food	Portion	Grams
Cornmeal, dry	1/4 cup	29
Cornstarch	1 tbsp	7
Cowpeas, cooked	1 cup	25
Crab	1 lb.	2
Cracker Meal	1 tbsp	7
Crackers:		
Rye Wafer	1 cracker	2
Ry-Krisp	1 dbl square	10
Saltine	1 cracker	3
Wheat Thins	1 cracker	1
Cranberries	1 cup	11
Cream, Heavy	1 tbsp	1
Cress, water	1 bunch	4
Croutons	1/2 in cubes	1
Cucumbers	6 slices	1
Currants	3/4 cup	14
Curry Powder	1 tsp	1
Dandelion Greens, cooked	1/2 cup	6
Dates	3 or 4	23
Duck	1 avg	0
Dumpling	1	6
Eels	1 srvg	0
Egg Foo Yung	1	7
Egg Roll	1/2 cup	4
Eggplant	1 med	6
Eggs	2 stalks	0
Endive	2 lg leaves	4
Escarole		2
Fats	1 tbsp	0
Fennel	2 pcs	2
Figs	2 sm	20
Figs, dried, cut	1 cup	64

CARBOHYDRATE LISTINGS

Food	Portion	Grams
Filberts	10 to 12	3
Fish Sticks, frozen	4 oz	0
Flounder		0
Flour:		
Amaranth	1 cup	62
Arrowroot	1 cup	56
Barley	1 cup	120
Beau	1 cup	63
Cake	1 cup	72
Chestnut	1 cup	112
Corn	1 cup	114
Cornmeal	1 cup	120
Cornstarch	1 cup	56
Cottonseed	1 cup	99
Millet	1 cup	114
Potato	1 cup	160
Rice	1 cup	86
Rye	1 cup	62
Soybean	1 cup	38
Tapioca, dry	1 cup	122
Wheat	1 cup	84
White	1 cup	84
Frankfurters		1
Frog Legs		4
Fruit Cocktail	1 cup	34
Garlic, peeled	1 oz	9
Gefilite Fish	4 oz	4
Gelatin, plain	1 tbsp	0
Goose		0
Gooseberries	1 cup	13
Grapefruit, fresh	1/2 lg	22
Grapes	1 cup	15
Grits, Hominy,		
cooked	1/2 cup	13
Gauva	1	17

CARBOHYDRATE LISTINGS

Food	Portion	Grams
Haddock, baked	3 oz	0
Halibut, broiled	3 oz	0
Ham		1
Hash, Cornbeef	3 oz	8
Hazelnuts	10 to 12	3
Head Cheese	3 oz	0
Herbs		0
Hickory Nuts	15 small	2
Honeydew Melon	1 wedge	13
Horseradish		0
Huckleberries	1 cup	21
Ice Cream:		
Chocolate	1/4 pint	17
Sherbet, with milk	1/4 pint	45
Jams, Jellies	1 tbsp	14
Juices, Fruit	1 cup	35
Juices:		
Lemon	1 tbsp	1
Lemon	1 cup	20
Lime	1 tbsp	1
Lime	1 cup	22
Sauerkraut	1 cup	8
Tomato, canned	1 cup	10
Vegetable, canned	1 cup	9
Kale, cooked	1 cup	7
Kidneys	1/2 cup	1
Kohlrabi, cooked	1 cup	10
Kumquats	5 or 6	10
Lamb		0
Lambsquarter	1/2 cup	8
Lard		0
Leeks	3 med	8
Lemon	1 med	5

27

CARBOHYDRATE LISTINGS

Food	Portion	Grams
Lentils	1/2 cup	22
Lettuce	1 head	5
Lettuce, shredded	1 cup	3
Lichee Nuts	6	11
Lime	1 med	2
Liver	2 oz	3
Liverwurst	1 slice	1
Lobster, fresh with		
2 tbsp butter	3/4 lb	1
Loganberries	2/3 cup	15
Lox (smoked salmon)		0
Luncheon Meats	1 oz	1
Macadamia Nuts	10 to 12	2
Macaroni, cooked	1 cup	32
Mackerel		0
Mango	1 med	35
Margarine	1 tbsp	0
Melon Balls	1 cup	13
Meringue	1/4 cup	8
Milk, whole	1 cup	12
Milk, nonfat	1 cup	13
Milk, Chocolate	1 cup	25
Millet, grain	1 cup	72
Muffins	1 med	21
Mushrooms	4 lg	4
Muskmelon	1/2 med	8
Mussels	1 lb	7
Mustard, dry		0
Mustard Greens,		
cooked	1 cup	6
Nectarines	1 med	8
Noodles, Egg, cooked	1 cup	37
Noodles, fried,		
canned	1 oz	17
Nuts, mixed	8 to 12	3

CARBOHYDRATE LISTINGS

Food	Portion	Grams
Oils		0
Okra, cooked	8 pods	6
Olives, green/black	10 lg	1
Onions, raw	1 med	11
Onions, green	6 sm	5
Oranges, fresh	1 med	17
Ovaltine	1 cup	22
Oysters, raw	1 cup	8
Pancakes, buckwheat	1-4"	9
Papaya, cubes	1 cup	18
Parsley, chopped	1 tbsp	0
Parsnips, cooked	1/2 cup	11
Pastrami		0
Peaches, fresh	1 med	3
Peanut Butter	1 tbsp	3
Peanuts	1 cup	27
Pears, fresh	1 med	24
Peas, fresh, cooked	1 cup	19
Peas, split, cooked	1 cup	20
Pecans	2	2
Peppers, green	1 med	3
Peppers, red	1 med	4
Perch, fresh		0
Persian Melon	1 wedge	13
Pheasant		0
Pickle Relish	1 tbsp	3
Pickles, cucumber	6 slices	1
Pie (average)	1-4" slice	47
Pike		0
Pimiento, canned	1 med	2
Pine Nuts, salted	1/2 cup	6
Pineapple, fresh, diced	1 cup	19
Pistachio Nuts	20	2
Plums, fresh	1 med	7

CARBOHYDRATE LISTINGS

Food	Portion	Grams
Popcorn, popped	1 cup	11
Popover	1	3
Pork		0
Potato Chips	8 to 10	10
Potatoes:		
Baked or Boiled	1 med	21
French Fried	10 pcs	20
Hash Browned	1 cup	62
Flour	4 oz	80
Sweet, baked	1	36
Yams, cooked	1 cup	48
Pretzels	1 g	13
Prunes	4 med	19
Puddings (average)	1/2 cup	14
Quail, broiled		0
Quince	1 med	10
Rabbit		0
Radishes	5	2
Raisins, dried	1 tbsp	8
Raspberries	1 cup	20
Red Snapper		0
Rhubarb, raw, diced	1 cup	5
Rice, brown, cooked	1 cup	43
Rice Flour	1 cup	86
Rice, wild, cooked	1 cup	30
Rolls (average)	1 roll	21
Romaine	1 lg leaf	0
Rutabaga, cooked	1 cup	12
Salad Dressings	1 tbsp	1 (approx)
Salads:		
Apple-Carrot	1/2 cup	12
Asparagus	5 spears	4

CARBOHYDRATE LISTINGS

Food	Portion	Grams
Salads:		
Avocado w/dressing	1/2 cup	0
Carrot Raisin	3 tbsp	28
Cole Slaw	1/2 cup	7
Chicken w/celery	1/2 cup	2
Egg and Tomato	1/2 each	4
Lettuce and Tomatoes	1/2 cup	6
Mixed Greens w/		
French drssg	1/2 cup	5
Potato w/onions	1/2 cup	13
Shrimp w/celery	1/2 cup	5
Tomato and cucumber	1 each	10
Tuna	1/2 cup	3
Salami	8 oz	3
Salmon		0
Sardines, canned,		
oil		0
Sardines, canned,		
tomato sauce	1 lg	1
Sauces:		
A-1	1 tbsp	3
Barbecue	1 tbsp	8
Chili	1 tbsp	4
Hollandaise (true)	1/4 cup	0
Mustard	1/4 cup	6
Sour Cream	1 tbsp	4
Soy	1 tbsp	2
Tartar	1 tbsp	2
Tomato	1/4 cup	6
White, medium	1/4 cup	6
Worchestershire	1 tbsp	3
Sauerkraut, drained	1 cup	7
Sausage, Polish	4 oz	1
Scallops	2 to 3	3
Sesame Seeds	1 oz	0
Shad		0

CARBOHYDRATE LISTINGS

Food	Portion	Grams
Shrimp, fresh	3 oz	1
Smelt		0
Snow Peas (pods)	14 to 16	6
Sole		0
Soda, Seltzer Water		0
Soups:		
Bean	3/4 cup	19
Bouillon	3/4 cup	0
Celery	3/4 cup	7
Chicken Broth	3/4 cup	0
Chili Beef	3/4 cup	19
Clam Chowder, Milk	3/4 cup	14
Clam Chowder,		
tomato	3/4 cup	8
Consomme	3/4 cup	0
Corn Chowder	3/4 cup	19
Onion	3/4 cup	4
Onion, French	3/4 cup	4
Split Pea	3/4 cup	17
Tomato, clear	3/4 cup	12
Tomato Vegetable	3/4 cup	11
Vegetable Beef	3/4 cup	7
Vichyssoise	3/4 cup	12
Soybean Milk	3/8 cup	2
Soybean Sprouts	1 cup	11
Spaghetti, cooked	1 cup	44
Spices	1 tsp	0
Spinach, raw	1/2 lb.	0
Spinach, cooked	1 cup	6
Squab		0
Squash:		
Hubbard or Winter,		
baked	1/2 cup	11
Summer, cooked	1 cup	8
Squid		0

32

CARBOHYDRATE LISTINGS

Food	Portion	Grams
Stew, Beef and		
Vegetable	1 cup	19
Strawberries, fresh	5 lg	4
Sturgeon		0
Sugar:		
Granulated	1 cup	199
Granulated	1 tbsp	12
Sweetbreads		0
Swordfish		0
Syrups:		
Chocolate	1 tbsp	12
Corn	1 tbsp	15
Honey	1 tbsp	16
Maple	1 tbsp	13
Tangerines	1 med	10
Tapioca	1/4 cup	33
Tea	1 cup	0
Toast, Melba	1 slice	4
Tomatoes, Fresh	1 med	6
Tomatoes, Canned	1 cup	9
Tortilla, 5" dia	1	5
Tripe, boiled		0
Trout, brook		0
Tuna		0
Turkey		0
Turnip Greens, cooked	1 cup	8
Turnips, diced	1 cup	9
Turtle		0
Vanilla Extract	1/2 tsp	0
Veal		0
Venison		0
Vinegar	1 tbsp	1

33

CARBOHYDRATE LISTINGS

Food	Portion	Grams
Waffles, 5-1/2"	1	30
Walnuts, halves	8 to 10	3
Walnuts, chopped	1 cup	18
Watermelon, 4 x 8" wedge	1	29
Wheat Germ	1 tbsp	4
White fish, steamed or smoked		0
Yogurt, skim milk	1 cup	13

IDEAL DIETS VERSES REAL DIETS

"Ideal" diets are printed with a lot of do's, but mostly don'ts by well meaning folks. By following the instructions exactly you will achieve your goals. The closer one stays to the diet, the sooner one gets well.

"Sally Sez:" The stricter one stays with the diet, the sooner one may get bored with it and **quits**. Then begin to feel guilty, and or resentful which increases stress and slows down healing.

A major contributing factor to our dis-eases are distresses. Selye describes stress as ". . . the bodies struggle to adapt to a noxious agent . . ." That "noxious agent" may be a family member, an associate, your boss, polluted air, artificial lighting, preservatives in food, artificial colorings, candida yeast infestation, food allergies or any number of things including a strict diet..

THE PERFECT DIET is organically grown (no chemicals or pesticides), raw or barely steamed vegetables, fresh fruit (when allowed), sprouts, fish, poultry, (no red meat), raw nuts and raw seeds served in a loving and relaxed atmosphere, totally free of stress, conflict or pollution.

Circumstances seldom allow the perfect meal once a day, let alone three times. But please do follow it as closely as you can, whenever you can.

The Ideal Diet is the perfect meal which looks wonderful on paper, but so difficult to   follow it isn't realistic. **The Real Diet** is what you can follow day after day. Although it's not the perfect, it's the one we can live with long enough to achieve our goals. It may take longer to get well, but we'll <u>stay</u> <u>on</u> <u>it</u> <u>long</u> <u>enough</u> to finally get healthy.

Fast Food Eateries are **real**, sad but true, so let's deal with them: <u>Fish</u> <u>&</u> <u>Chips</u> - Find one in your area with 'chunks' rather than flat fillets, so when the coating is peeled off you can find the fish. Complete the meal with a trip to the salad bar. However, if not available, the addition of lots of cole slaw and a 'few' french fried potatoes would be OK.

At the salad bar oil and vinegar or Italian dressing are the least problem usually, the others have sugars which feed the yeast. Vinegar may produce unpleasant allergic reactions, but it doesn't feed the yeast.

<u>Ketchup</u> is one-third (1/3) sugar, tartar sauce has less, and they both contain vinegar. So let kids have small amounts, if they insist. Lemon juice is best.

<u>Taco</u> <u>Time/Taco</u> <u>Bell</u> - Peel a burrito and eat the middle only, discard the shell as it is made of corn or wheat. <u>Tostadas</u> are flat tacos with the filling pilled on top, and is easier to eat than disecting a taco, just don't eat the tortilla on the bottom. Chili is okay and so is a Taco Salad.

Pizza Parlors - Eat the topping only, not the crust. Have a side order of meatballs or salad if it is available.

Fried Chicken - Peel chicken as you would a piece of fish. A side of beans or a three bean salad is a wiser choice than potatoes or biscuits.

Burgers - Eat the middle of a hamburger or a cheeseburger. Again, any type of salad or vegetable you can order on the side is a wiser choice than buns, or bread or biscuits.

Seven - Eleven/Stop 'n Go - in the middle of the night or early in the morning? Warm up a burrito in the microwave and eat the middle with a spoon. Popcorn is usually a better choice than a donut. Peanuts, sunflower seeds and beef jerky although it is full of preservatives are emergency suggestions that would be far better than a Danish roll.

I am not recommending that you eat this way. These suggestions are for emergencies only.

Also see Brown Bag Ideas for travel, outings and social events.

HOW TO CLEAN FOODS

Molds are naturally present in or on most foods, and since we are sensitive to those critters, we need to remove as much as possible in order to avoid allergic reactions. Cleaning also eliminates some of the chemicals, pesticides, preservatives and other undesirable substances in our food.

Clorox Soak - My chemically sensitive clients seem to tolerate their foods better after this cleansing process. It's very well worth the time and effort.

Step #1: 1 tsp. liquid Clorox to 2 gallons of water (use the Clorox brand **only**). Place fresh fruits, vegetables, meat or fish in the bath. Soak 15 minutes for most foods; 20 minutes for heavy skinned foods. Timing is important.

After filling the container (sink, bucket, or wash tub) with water, mark the 2 gallon level with a piece of tape so you don't have to re-measure each time.

Try wearing a clip or noseplugs if you are sensitive to the odor.

Step #2: Remove food and soak in bath of clean water for 15 minutes. Drain and store. If odor is too strong, add 1/4 cup of vinegar, or 1/4 cup baking soda to the rinse water.

Additional benefits of the soak: Melons and root vegetables, etc. that we couldn't previously tolerate due to the mold and pesticides, may be OK to eat now. Foods taste fresher, and wilted vegetables get crisp and stay fresh longer. Drain, wrap in paper towels or clean cloth, place in storage bag and refrigerate.

Antibiotics are added to the ice that fish is packed in when caught, so it is important to use the soak or at least to rinse well under running water.

If you don't always have time for the soak, then scrub all fruits and vegetables with soap and water, then rinse well.

Peeling root vegetables may remove some of the mold, but it also just spreads it around, so clean it first!

Melons especially need to be cleaned. When we cut into a melon, squash or pumpkin, the blade drags the mold into the flesh.

Roasting nuts lightly seems to make them more tolerable for it 'kills' some of the live spores of the molds and reduces "allergenicity". Place in baking pan or cookie sheet and bake at 300 F. about 10 minutes. Stir frequently to avoid burning. You may roast your nuts slightly longer if you prefer, but heat can also destroy the fatty acids, 'the good stuff' in nuts, so the shorter the roasting time, the better.

Socializing - Dinner Parties

Yes, you can enjoy an evening with friends. There are times when one must be a bit devious and clever, depending on your relationship with the host or hostess.

Good Friends understand (or will try atleast) when hearing you need to avoid sauces, casseroles and noodles. Tell them fish, chicken, turkey, roast beef, anything simple with a vegetable and a tossed green will be fine. Bring whatever type of "munchie" you can tolerate (raw vegies, or a chip you can tolerate), plus a dip, mineral water, if desired so you don't feel left out when others are nibbling on pretzels and cheese.

Strangers or those who can't or won't understand don't need to know. Eat before you go if you don't know the menu in advance. Offer to bring something i.e. a new dip recipe. Then, of course take along the dippers (raw vegetables, potato chips, carrot chips, etc.) Fresh roasted nuts are always welcome snack food.

Find yourself dealing with an 'alcohol pusher' or a person who thinks allergies or Candida are "all in your mind"? Tell them that the medication you're taking doesn't mix with alcohol. It's sad but true that prescription drugs are generally accepted while allergies are not. Attempting to explain a yeast infection may prove to be a waste of time.

Don't feel like you have to apologize and don't be afraid to say "no thank you."

Dining Out

How far you can stray off the diet depends on several things. Among the most important are: how _often_ one cheats, how _far off_ the diet you wandered, the type of food you cheated on, how much you ate of it, and the degree of your sensitivities to those foods.

A rare special occasion allows for greater indulgence than cheating "just a little" every day.

Choose baked, broiled or sauteed fish, poultry or meats without sauces. (It is usually acceptable when dining out to ask for sauces and salad dressings on the side, then simply don't use it.) If nothing appeals to you on the main entrees order from the appetizer or a la carte sections.

A seafood cocktail (sauce on the side), salad (spinach, tossed green, ceasar, coleslaw or sliced tomato with dressing on the side), perhaps an antipasto dish, a vegetable such as even a baked potato makes a well rounded meal, satisfying meal. Say "No thank you" to rolls and pasta.

Breakfast is the most difficult restaurant meal if allergic to wheat, milk and eggs -- especially while avoiding grains. Perhaps a ground beef patty, side order of ham, sausage, bacon, or potatoes may be your safest choices. Fresh melon is usually available, but consider the possibility of molds. Tuna or chicken salads are sometimes made up ahead of time and available. Pray that the chef is congenial and co-operative, think positively and ask but don't count on it.

Breakfast Suggestions

Ground beef patty
Amaranth muffins*
Pecan butter*

Pork chop
Amaranth Pancakes
Pecan butter*
and chopped pecans

Millet-Sunflower
seed-carrot
casserole*

Eggs and
hashbrowns

Nut loaf with
almond butter*

Bean cakes* topped
with almond butter
chopped almonds

Veggie Nut Loaf
Nut muffins

Pork chop or ground
pork patty & baked
sweet potato topped
with chopped nuts

Sunflower seed
wedge* with
sunflower butter

Nut pancakes with
Sesame butter* &
chopped filberts

Chicken and refried
beans w/corn
tortillas*

Mashed squash or
pumpkin patties with
chopped nuts*

Arrowroot-cashew*
pancakes topped with
cashew butter &
chopped cashews

Nutri-ola cereal
or bars*

*See recipes in this book

Lunch Suggestions

Turkey- celery
salad*

Turkey vegetable
soup*

Tofuna* or tuna
salad with raw
vegetables

Shrimp Salad*

Shrimp-vegetable
dish* with fresh
beet borscht

Garlic soup* or
Carrot soup* with
  marinated vegies

Soybean stew*

Hearty salad*

Vegetable soup*

Stuffed Tomatoes*
& clam broth

Turkey pie*

Crab Bisque with

Russian salad I or
Russian salad II*

Broccoli soup*

Shellfish cocktail*

Seafood Bisque*

Large Green Salad
& leftover meats or
poultry or seafood

Carrot-jicama salad*

*See recipes. See additional ideas under Brown Bag Ideas. Compliment the main
dishes with crackers, muffins, crepes, nutri-ola bars, raw & cooked vegetables.

YUM--DELICIOUS TREATS
*** Clean and freeze cut-up pieces of fresh fruit, canned pineapple chunks, grapes
    peeled bananas, berries, etc. Pop them into your mouth like a mini popsicle.

Dinner Suggestions

Korean broiled
steak* with
blushed cauliflower*
green salad

Beef roast
baked potato
spinach salad*

Veal a la mode*
beansprouts &
seed hot
vegetable dish*

Herbed baked fish*
Neapolitan
zucchini*
coleslaw

Rabbit Stew*

Old-fashioned Pot
roast* broccoli with
with walnut butter
tossed green salad

Savory stuffed
peppers*

Broiled fish*

Seafood Bisque*

Seafood Ragout*

Bouillabaisse*

Stuffed Fish Fillets*

Turkey Pie*

Ponset*
savory beans and
onions* and jellied
tomato salad

Lemon broiled
chicken and
spiced eggplant*
green salad

Green beans with
hamburger* and
marinated vegetables

Sweet & Sour stuffed
cabbage
3-bean salad

Sole Almadine*
*see recipes.

Add any vegetable, cracker, muffin or bread allowed to the main dishes. See the
Crock-pot Cookery section for additional ideas.

Vegetarian (*vegan*) Menu Plans

Day 1 Green day	Day 2 Yellow day	Day 3 Blue day	Day 4 Red day
SESAME PANCAKES with SESAME BUTTER	BEAN CAKES with ALMOND BUTTER OR SUNFLOWER WEDGE	VEGGIE NUT LOAF	ARROWROOT/CASHEW PANCAKES with CASHEW BUTTER or, HURRY UP HASH
COLE SLAW CURRIED LENTILS	SPINACH SALAD PEASANT VEGETABLE SOUP RICE CAKES	3-BEAN SALAD ONION SOUP FALAFEL	STUFFED TOMATO HOT & SOUR SOUP AVOCADO MOUSSE
GARLIC SOUP SESAME CUC. SALAD BROC. WALNUT DELIGHT FALAFEL	RUSSIAN SALAD II ALMOND SOUP BAKED POTATO GADO GADO SAUCE	GALA SALAD MINESTRONE PONSET	HEARTY SALAD GUACAMOLE S. STUFFED PEPPERS BAKED SWEET POTATO

Sip herbal teas throughout the day, preferrably between meals.

Eat small, frequent meals, and/or snackon raw veggies , nuts & seeds -- see page 7.

BROWN BAG AND LUNCH IDEAS

Plan ahead to do what you can to have lunch ready the night before and avoid early morning hassles.

1. Prepare an extra batch of pancakes (see pages 167-9) ahead of time and fill with a variety of spreads. Roll or stack them for variety.

2. Maintain a supply of novelty napkins, utensils and small containers. Add special notes, jokes or riddles frequently.

3. Include foods for children that you **know** they enjoy. Do the testing at home.

4. Handy supplies include: Wide mouth thermos are ideal for soup, stew, salads, puddings, etc. Place hot water and 'acceptable' hot dog in thermos. Cold pack by packing 'blue ice' in the bottom of the lunch bag, or use an old flat plastic lotion bottle. Fill bottle 3/4 full of water, freeze and place in plastic bag and seal.

5. Keep an S.O.S. lunch at school or office for emergencies. Nutri-ola bars are usually a favorite, bags of nuts or seeds, crackers and nut butters, cans of sardines, other home canned foods and other non-perishable will be welcome. If a freezer is available make use of it also.

6. Put in extras occasionally for your child to **share** not trade.

7. Freeze small quantities of meats, poultry, crackers, spreads, etc. and package individually. Put these into the lunch bag at the last minute, they will be cold but thawed by lunch time. Save shoe boxes and use for storing sandwiches in the freezer so they don't get squashed.

8. Pack lettuce leaves separately to avoid wilting. Use sprouts for fun and variety. See page 51 for sprouting directions.

9. See recipes and menu plans for a variety of fillings, salads and hot or cold one-dish meals. This variety will keep lunch interesting.

10. The best time to pack lunch is right after dinner. Place left overs in small containers and refrigerate or freeze right away.

11. Take one afternoon a week (or a month) to bake acceptable muffins, cookies, crackers and crusts. Pack small quantities of nuts to eat like 'trail mix'. Ask the lunch eaters to plan their own menus occasionally and to give you their ideas.

12. Allergy-free protein powders can be nutritious, time saving staples for use every day, or for "quickie" meals. The trick is to find them pure enough for us sensitive individuals. Contact me for up-to-date list and SMOOTHIE recipes.

'Sandwich' Fillings

This is just a limited list to stir your imagination and get the creative juices (and the digestive juices) flowing.

Mix and match nut butters with all sorts of chopped vegetables, sprouts, nuts or seeds. Spread on a pancake, roll up and enjoy.

Have a 'burrito' for breakfast, made with a bean pan cake and refried beans.

Make additional 'cakes', stack them with paper towels or waxed paper in between so they don't stick together. Good for snacking, brown bag lunches, traveling, even desserts for special occasions, like "crepes".

Anything edible and/or spreadable can be sliced, mashed, chopped or ground with anything else and spread on a 'pancake'.

Nut Butters, Tunafish, Egg Salad, Chicken, Turkey, Ham, Beef, Pork, Lamb, Rabbit, Mashed Beans, Chopped or whole Nuts & Seeds, Chopped Vegetables, Sprouts, (see page 52).

Variety of food choices is MOST important for those with Candida and food allergies. Eating the same foods day after day is one of the reasons we have food allergies. Milk, wheat and eggs, which have been our traditional daily morning meal has to change. So consider foods we usually eat for lunch or dinner.

Basic Ingredients for Fillings, Spreads and Dips

(See recipes for specific dishes)

Make Nut Butters from:
almonds, cashews, filberts (hazel nuts), macadamia nuts, pecans, pistachios, pumpkin seeds, sesame seeds or sunflower seeds.

combine with:
any chopped, cooked meat, poultry or seafood, i.e.:

tuna	cooked,
sardines	mashed,
turkey	beans
shrimp	tofu
chicken	
rabbit	
beef	
sole	

combine with:
any chopped or grated-raw or cooked vegetables, i.e.:

chopped:	grated:
celery	parsnips
olives*	carrots
pickles*	turnips
onions	jicama
sprouts	coconut
radishes	avocado
cucumbers	
green or red peppers	
water chestnuts	
bamboo shoots	cabbage
parsley	tomatoes

If too dry, add water, oil, creamed cheese, mayonaise (if tolerated), or any tolerated salad dressing or sauce, until desired consistency.

NOTES

Enjoy the World of Sprouting

Sprouts are the tiny shoots that emerge from seeds, beans or grains on the way to becoming mature plants. Sprouting turns low cost seeds into tiny dynamos of energy, rich in vitamins, minerals, enzymes and other important food values. They can be easily grown in your own kitchen without chemicals or pesticides. The most popular are alfalfa seeds, mung beans, lentils, & fenugreek. I like cabbage, radish or mustard seed sprouts mixed together for a sprouted cole slaw; or any of them mixed in other salads for a "zippy" taste treat.

To grow your own sprouts, place them in a quart jar, then cover with warm water and soak overnight. Cover the top with cheesecloth or a piece of screen, and secure with a rubber band. Drain off the soaking water (good to water your houseplants with), then rinse with fresh lukewarm water and drain again. Turn the jar on its side until sprouts appear; then place in sunlight if desired to develop green sprouts.

Mung bean sprouts turn brown unless kept in the dark, so cover the jar with a brown paper sack to protect from the light. Rinse as directed.

It is important to rinse the sprouts 2 or more times each day. In 2 to 5 days they will be ready, at which time they should be placed in the refrigerator where they will keep for several days. Store them right in the jar.

Sprouts can be eaten raw or cooked or steamed. Use in salads, sandwiches, main dishes, omelettes or chop suey.

SPROUTING GUIDE

Variety of seed	Quantity of seed	Soaking Time (hours)	Rinse & Drain (#/daily)	Average Time to Harvest (days/inches)	Suggested Uses
Alfalfa	2 T.	6 to 8	2	3 to 6 days 1 to 2"	salads sandwiches juices
Chinese Cabbage	1 cup	6 to 8	2	3 to 4 days 1/2 to 1"	salads juices
Fenugreek	1 cup	6 to 8	2 to 3	3 to 4 days 1/2 to 1-1/2"	salads snacks
Garbanzo	1 cup	16	2 to 3	3 to 6 days 1//8 to 1"	salads soup stir-fry casseroles
Lentil	1/2 cup	8 to 12	2 to 3	2 to 3 days 1/4 to 1"	salads snacks. soups casseroles
Mung Beans	1/2 cup	8 to 12	2 to 3	2 to 4 days 1/4 to 1"	salads, soups stir-fry

SPROUTING GUIDE

Variety of seed	Quantity of seed	Soaking Time (hours)	Rinse & Drain (#/daily)	Average Time to Harvest (days/inches)	Suggested Uses
Peas	1/2 or 1 cup	8 to 12	2 to 3	2 to 3 days 1/2 to 1"	salads soups stir-fry
Radish	2 T. or 1 cup	6 to 8	2	3 to 4 days 1/2 to 1"	salads juices sandwiches
Red Clover	2 T.	8	2	3 to 6 days 1/2 to 2-1/2"	salads sandwiches juices
Sesame	1/4 cup	8	2	1 to 3 days 0 to 1"	breads desserts snacks
Soybean	1/2 or 1 cup	16	3	3 to 5 days 1/2 to 1"	casseroles soups stir-fry
Sunflower (hulled)	1/2 or 1 cup	6 to 8	2	1 to 2 days 0 to 1/2"	salads, snacks desserts

CURRIED LENTILS

4 cups cooked lentils
1 large sliced onion
2 tablespoons safflower oil
2 tablespoons mild curry powder (more or less to taste)
1 cup sliced carrots
2 cups diced potatoes
1-1/2 cups water
1 cup minced parsley (1/2 cup dried parsley)

Saute onion in oil. Stir in curry powder. Add carrots and potatoes. Continue stirring, Gradually add water and remaining ingredients, simmer vegetables until tender, add lentils.

Sprinkle with parsley before serving.

The longer this simmers, the better the flavor. Tastes great without the carrots and potatoes, also.

SAVORY GREEN BEANS   Yield: 4 portions**

1/2 lb. fresh snap beans cut into 1" pieces
1 teaspoon tarragon leaves
1/2 teaspoon salt
1/8 teaspoon ground black pepper
1 tablespoon lemon juice
2-1/2 cups sliced onion

Place beans in a saucepan containing 1" boiling water, tarragon, black pepper and lemon juice. Cook, uncovered for 5 minutes. Add onions. Reduce heat and simmer covered for 5 minutes or until beans are tender.

I often cook 2 pounds of vegetables and eat the whole thing all by myself. Make an entire meal out of vegetables whenever possible. Your body will love you for it.

BLUSHED CAULIFLOWER

Yield: 4 portions

1 medium size head cauliflower
1 teaspoon tarragon leaves, crumbled
1/2 teaspoon salt
1/16 teaspoon ground white pepper
1/2 teaspoon paprika

Wash cauliflower thoroughly; remove outer leaves and core, keeping head intact. Place in 1" boiling water in a large saucepan or skillet. Add tarragon and white pepper. Add cauliflower and cook for 10 minutes basting frequently with tarragon flavored liquid. Cover, reduce heat and simmer 15 to 20 minutes longer or until tender. Carefully remove cauliflower to serving dish. Dust with paprika.

Notes:

SPICED EGGPLANT

Yield: 4 portions

2-1/2 cups peeled, diced, uncooked eggplant
1-1/2 cups diced celery
1/2 chopped onion
3/4 teaspoon powdered mustard
3/4 teaspooon ground turmeric
1/2 teaspoon salt
1/8 teaspoon ground ginger
1 tablespoon lemon juice
Dash cayenne to taste

Saute eggplant, onion and celery in 2 tbsp. oil in a medium sized sauce-pan.

Add 3/4 cups water and the remaining ingredients. Cover and simmer over low heat about 10 minutes or until the water has evaporated and vegetables are tender.

MARINATED VEGETABLES

(Double recipe, it keeps well)

1/3 cup lemon juice
1 or 2 cloves garlic, slivered
1 teaspoon dried salad herbs and seasonings
1/2 cup cold-pressed vegetable oil
2 lbs. (total) vegetables, sprouts, tofu cubes and/or cooked beans

(May use frozen veggies right out of the package, do not cook)

1/2 teaspoon salt (optional)

In a small saucepan combine lemon juice, garlic and herbs. Simmer very gently for about 5 minutes. Cover and set aside to steep. Add oil when luke warm.

Cut vegetables into bite-sized pieces. Hard vegetables such as cauliflower, broccoli or green beans may be lightly steamed first, while others such as cucumber, zucchini or sweet onion are best if left raw. Bite sized pieces of raw tofu are delicious marinated, as are large beans such as chick peas or kidney beans (cook until tender but not falling apart, and drain).

Toss all ingredients in a large bowl. Some scallion, or fresh herbs make a nice addition at this point. Pour marinade evenly over the vegetables and toss again. Let sit at least 1 hour, best overnight, to develop full flavor. Toss from time to time to mix marinade with veggies, or marinate under pressure by placing a weighted dish on top of them inside the bowl. (A jug full of water makes a good weight).

Note: Marinated veggies can be mixed into salads, served as pickles or as a side dish. They make a nice winter salad and are a delicious accompaniment to fish, chicken, meat and non-vegetarian main dishes.

When you can tolerate some carbohydrates, add cooked whole, quinoa, amaranth, brown rice, millet or buckwheat groats, toss gently. A great main dish, and a good traveler for picnics, pot-lucks, pitch-ins.

Will keep for a week or more refrigerated, the flavor continues to develop with age.

Seasonings: Any fresh or dried salad herb, i.e.: parsley, basil, marjoram, dill, celery seed, fennel or caraway. Also try a little powdered dulse or kelp bay leaf, peppercorns, ginger, curry or cayenne.

SOPHISTICATED VEGETABLES

2 cups cooked, chopped string beans
1/2 cup water chestnuts, sliced
1 cup cauliflower, sliced thin
2 tablespoons onion, dried
1/2 cup beets, sliced thin

1/4 cup lemon juice
1/3 cup sesame oil
1 teaspoon salt
1/4 teaspoon garlic powder

Combine lemon, oil, and spices and mix well. Toss with remaining ingredients.
Serve "as is" or over greens or sprouts.
Make ahead of time, flavor improves on standing.

When you can tolerate some carbohydrates, add cooked whole quinoa, amaranth,
millet, brown rice, or buckwheat groats. toss gently. Serve as a complete meal
or a side dish.

MEALS WITH A K.I.S.S. (Keep It Simple, Sweetie)

Steam a fresh vegetable, or place frozen vegetable in small saucepan, cover and
heat slowly while steaming or saute'ing a piece of fish (page 127-129).
Sprinkle with seasoned salt (page 72) if desired.

CRAB BISQUE

1/2 cup frozen black-eyed peas
1/2 cup sliced white squash
1/3 cup crab meat, cooked or canned
Dash paprika

Cover peas and squash with water and simmer until tender. Add crab meat and run mixture through the blender. Sprinkle with paprika, reheat and season to taste.

SESAME VEGETABLES

2 cups of chopped vegetables:
    See page seven for ideas. Try swiss chard, cabbage, broccoli, kale, nappa, squash, carrots, celery, onion, string beans, etc.

1 tablespoon unrefined sesame oil
1/2 cup sesame seeds
Sesame salt to taste (or use sea salt)

Cook vegetables until tender but crisp. Drain. Heat oil in skillet. Add sesame seeds and stir until sizzling. Carefully add vegetables and gently heat through. Season to taste.

BEANSPROUT DELIGHT

Preheat Oven: 375^0

2 tablespoons oil
1/2 cup sesame seeds, ground
1/2 cup chopped nuts (almonds, filberts, cashews, pistachios, etc)
1 tablespoon salt
1 clove garlic, minced
3 cups mung bean sprouts
1 cup summer squash, cubed
1 small onion, chopped
1 tablespoon salt if desired to taste

Pour oil into a large flat pan. Add the seeds, chopped nuts, 1 tablespoon of salt and garlic. Toss gently and bake at 375^0 for 5 to 8 minutes. Steam bean sprouts for 2 to 3 minutes. Saute squash and onion and combine with sprouts.

Pour topping over sprout mixture and serve.

GREEN BEANS AND BURGER

3/4 lb. ground beef, turkey or chicken
1 medium onion, sliced
1/4 teaspoon garlic powder
1-1/2 cups water
1/2 teaspoon salt (optional)
1 lb. cut-up green beans. OR
     1 package (9 oz.) frozen green beans
3 tablespoons arrowroot
1/4 cup water
3 cups cooked mung bean noodles

Saute beef (or whatever) and onion in large skillet. Drain off the fat.
Add garlic powder, 1-1/2 cups water and salt, if desired, mix well.
Bring to a boil.
Add frozen green beans and simmer 5 minutes.
Blend arrowroot and 1/4 water. Stir gradually into meat mixture.
Simmer, stirring constantly until mixture thickens.
Serve over mung bean noodles (or rice if tolerated).

NEAPOLITAN ZUCCHINI

Yield: 4 portions

1 lb. zucchini squash
1 lb. tomatoes, peeled and diced
1 teaspoon oregano leaves
1 teaspoon instant minced onion
1/2 teaspoon salt
1/2 teaspoon instant garlic powder
1/4 teaspoon coarsely ground black pepper

Slice squash crosswise into 1/2" thick rounds.

In a medium sized saucepan combine squash with remaining ingredients.

Cook, covered over medium heat until squash is tender, about 15 minutes.

NOTES:

SALAD DRESSINGS, SAUCES, NUT BUTTERS, SOUPS & SEASONINGS

(Commonly known as "condiments")

NOTE OF CAUTION:

The ketchup and barbeque sauce recipes call for tomato paste. If you are extremely sensitive to molds and yeast do not use any commercially processed juices or sauces.

Purchase fresh tomatoes, wash in the Clorox soak, (page 38) place in a large pot. Bring to a boil, then simmer several hours on low heat, uncovered until thick.

Use wherever tomato sauce or tomato paste are called for in a recipe.

Freeze or can for future use.

See Crock Pot cooking, page 149 for even simpler preparation.

NOTES

BASIC SALAD DRESSING

1 teaspoon salt (optional)
1/4 teaspoon black pepper
1 teaspoon dry mustard
dash of tabasco
1/4 cup lemon juice or Vit. C mixture**
2/3 cup oil

Mix well, store in refrigerator. Double the recipe for convenience.

**Lemon juice or vinegar substitute: 1 TBSP. ascorbic acid (powdered vit. C) in
        1/4 cup water.

NOTE: For THICK or CREAMY dressing, add 1 tsp. guar gum or 1/2 tsp. xanthan gum,
blend thoroughly, let stand five minutes, blend again (see page 159)

GREEN GODDESS DRESSING

1 small can of anchovy fillets, mashed
1 green onion
handful of parsley
10 leaves fresh tarragon, or 2 teaspoons dried
2 cups BASIC SALAD DRESSING

Blend in a blender until smooth. Serve over crisp greens, sprouts, etc..

FRENCH DRESSING

1/2 teaspoon paprika
1 teaspoon sweetener (optional)
1/8 teaspoon pepper
1/2 teaspoon dried herbs (to taste)

1 teaspoon xanthan or guar gum (opt.)
1/3 cup lemon juice (or substitute)**
2/3 cup oil
1 teaspoon salt (optional)

**Lemon juice or vinegar substitute: 1 TBSP. ascorbic acid (powdered vit. C) in 1/4 cup water.

Combine all ingredients in a jar with a tight fitting lid; shake vigorously (or mix in a blender). Refrigerate.
Double amounts if desired. This dressing keeps well in the refrigerator. Be creative and consider adding: garlic, onions, anchovies. etc.

GUACAMOLE (Dip or Dressing)

1 large very ripe avocado
1 tomato chopped finely
1/4 teaspoon salt

1/8 cup lime juice
Chili powder to taste
Salt to taste (opt)

Mash avocado and mix with other ingredients. Use as a salad dressing or serve as a dip with tortillas or raw vegetables.
Excellent dressing for seafood salad.

HOMEMADE KETCHUP

Yield: 2 cups

2 cups home-made tomato paste (see p.65)
1/2 cup lemon juice (or sub. p.68)
1/2 cup water
1/2 teaspoon salt (optional)
1 teaspoon oregano

1/8 teaspoon cumin
1/8 teaspoon nutmeg
1/8 teaspoon pepper
1/2 teaspoon dry mustard
Dash garlic powder

Place all ingredients in blender, mix well. Keep refrigerated.

SEAFOOD (COCKTAIL) SAUCE

To Ketchup recipe above increase lemon juice to 1 cup, add 1 tbsp. horseradish (or to taste). Dash of tabasco sauce if desired.

ZESTY BARBECUE SAUCE

1 tablespoon oil
1 medium onion, chopped
1 clove garlic
1 cup **Homemade Ketchup**

1/2 cup water
1/2 teaspoon salt (optional)
Dash of tabasco
Dash of liquid smoke (optional)

In a saucepan, cook onion and garlic in oil until tender. Stir in remaining ingredients. Simmer covered for 10 minutes. Refrigerate remaining sauce for use later.

If grilling on a barbeque, add sauce during the last half of cooking to prevent scorching.

GADO-GADO SAUCE

An Indonesian dish with spicy tahini sauce

2 tablespoons sesame oil
1 cup onion, chopped
2 cloves garlic, crushed
1 to 2 teaspoons grated ginger
1 bay leaf

1 cup tahini (sesame butter)
1 tablespoon honey (opt)
1/8 teaspoon cayenne
Juice of 1 lemon (see sub. p.68)
1 teaspoon salt
3 cup water

Saute' oil, onion, garlic, and ginger in a saucepan. Add remaining ingredients. Mix thoroughly, simmer gently for 30 minutes.

Arrange a bed of cooked and raw vegetables on a platter. Start at the base with shredded cabbage, steamed asparagus and broccoli spears, whole green beans, mung bean sprouts and tofu chunks- plain or sauted in oil with sesame seeds.

Pour hot sauce over vegetables. Garnish with chopped nuts or seeds. ENJOY.

Get creative and have fun when arranging this dish. It's a great appetizer,a filling main dish or an eye-pleasing, tasty accompanyment to fish or poultry.

CLAM SOUP or SAUCE

1 clove garlic, crushed
1 onion, chopped
2 TBSP. arrowroot or tapioca starch
1/4 cube butter or 3 tablespoons oil
2-8 oz. cans minced clams, save juice
  salt to taste
Sprouts, bean threads (low carbohydrates) or
quinoa, rice or buckwheat noodles (high carbohydrates)

Saute garlic and onion in butter or oil, add arrowroot and mix well. Add the clam juice slowly, stirring constantly; simmer about 5 minutes. Add the clams just before serving. Heat only long enough to make it good and hot. Serve over sprouts or bean thread noodles.

The addition of a can of clam juice can turn this into a wonderful soup. Serve with home-made crackers (see page 161).

TASTY TOPPING

Preheat Oven: 375^0

3 TBSP vegetable oil
1/2 cup sesame seeds
1/2 cup chopped nuts or seeds)
1 tablespoon salt (optional)

1 clove garlic, minced
(or 1 tsp. garlic or onion powder)
&/or Add 1 tsp of a favorite herb)

Spread oil on a cookie sheet, mix all ingredients well, pour evenly on the oiled pan.   Bake 350 F, 10-15 minutes.   Stir often.
Make make a double batch and store in a glass jar in the refrigerator.

SESAME SALT*

1 cup sesame seeds (any seed or chopped nut)   1 teaspoon salt

Toast seeds until light brown in 325^0 oven, about 10 minutes. Stir often to avoid scorching. Place in blender with the salt, grind to a fine texture. Use in place of salt.

These are wonderful on cooked or raw vegetables, salads, home-made crackers, popcorn or in main dishes -- anything.

SALT-FREE TOPPING

Omit salt, sprinkle on waffles, pancakes, cereals, and as above.

NUT AND SEED BUTTERS, SPREADS AND MILKS

Almonds, Cashews, Coconut, Macadamia Nuts, Pecans, Pistachios, Brazil Nuts, Pumpkin Seeds, Sunflower Seeds, Sesame Seeds, Walnuts, Soy

A 'butter' or 'milk' can be made out of any kind of seed or nut, or combination. One cup of whole seeds or nuts yields about 1/2 cup of ground nut flour, or 'meal'. A seed/nut mill or grinder, a blender, or a food processor will produce a fine meal. Use according to manufacturer's instructions.

NUT BUTTER

After grinding nuts, just add oil, mix well, blend until smooth. Salt to taste.

DIP, SPREAD, OR SALAD DRESSING

Gradually add liquid to nut butter, stirring between additions, to desired consistency. Season to taste. Add chopped nuts or seeds as desired for crunch.

NUT OR SEED MILK

1/4 cup nut or seed meal with 8 oz. water. Blend until smooth. A pinch of salt, and/or 1 tsp sweetener may be added, if desired.

The flavor of butters, dips and spreads is improved by roasting the nuts or seeds before grinding. 1/3 roasted and 2/3 raw is a nice balance.

NOTES

ALMOND SOUP

2 cups blanched almonds
4 cups water
3 tablespoons oil
1 onion, (optional)
grated peel of 1 or 2 lemons
Seeds from 2 - 3 cardamon pods
1/2 teaspoon caraway seeds
Salt, to taste
1 cup soup stock

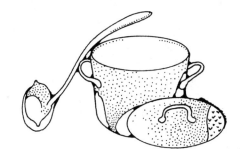

Combine all ingredients in a blender. Blend until smooth, pour mixture into a medium sized saucepan. Cover and simmer gently for 1 hour.

CLAM/AVOCADO DELIGHT

1-12 oz. can of clam juice
1 cup cashew meal (or 1/2 cup cashew butter)
1 finely diced medium avocado

Place clam juice and cashew meal or butter in blender, mix well, add avocado, heat but do not boil, garnish with topping on p.72.   Serve and enjoy.

FRESH BEET BORSCHT

1 medium onion, chopped
1 garlic clove, minced
1 turnip, diced
1 lb. fresh beets, shredded
Juice of one lemon, or
  1 tsp. ascorbic acid powder (vit C)
1/4 teaspoon salt
10 cups veg. broth
3 cups cabbage, shredded
Dill Weed

Combine onion, garlic, turnip, beets, lemon juice or vit. C, salt and broth in a large pan. Simmer for 30 minutes. Add   cabbage, simmer another 30 minutes. Garnish with spoonful of sour cream or yogurt, (if allowed). Sprinkle with dill weed and serve.

BROCCOLI/WALNUT DELIGHT

1 or 2 lb. broccoli
2 tbsp. butter
1/2 cup chopped walnuts
salt and pepper to taste

Use only the top of the broccoli stalks, save the bottom stem parts for broccoli soup   Steam floweretts or cook in small amount of boiling water in covered saucepan, 10 minutes or until crisp but tender. Drain well. Turn into serving bowl. While broccoli is cooking, melt butter in small skillet over medium to low heat. Add walnuts; cook slowly, stirring frequently. When butter begins to brown, add lemon juice, salt and pepper.
Pour mixture over hot broccoli, toss gently, serve immediately.

BROCCOLI SOUP

broccoli stems
1 cup chicken broth
1 cup heavy cream or 1/2 cup nut butter (cashew's my favorite)
Salt and pepper to taste   Dash of cayenne

Steam broccoli stems or cook covered, in a small amount of boiling slightlly salted water until tender, about 10 minutes. Puree stems in blender. Add chicken broth and heavy cream, mix well. Season with your favorite herbs. Gently heat, (do not allow soup to boil); serve hot or serve well chilled.

GARLIC SOUP
Wonderful for colds and flu!

1 large fresh head of garlic
1 quart water
2 cloves (optional)
1/2 bay leaf
pinch sage
pinch thyme

3 tablespoons olive oil
2 quarts chicken broth
3 cups beans, cooked
    kidney, soy, lima (optional)
1 cup stuffed green olives, sliced

Separate the cloves and peel by laying on a cutting board and slapping hard
with the flat side of a large-bladed knife or cleaver. Chop or mash and combine
with remaining ingredients. Simmer, covered, for 30 minutes.
Put through the blender, reheat, and serve. Garnish with olives.

Note: Blending is not necessary, it just makes the soup very special.

Notes:

HOT AND SOUR SOUP

6 cups stock
1/4 cup turnips, cut into thin strips
1/4 cup water chestnuts
1 lb. tofu, cubed
1 tablespoon lemon juice
1 teaspoon salt
1/2 teaspoon pepper
1 teaspoon honey
1/4 teaspoon cayenne
2 tablespoons arrowroot
4 tablespoons water
1 teaspoon sesame oil
2 green onions sliced
1 tablespoon corriander leaves, minced

Heat stock to boiling. Finely chop turnips, string beans, water chestnuts. Add to stock. Turn down heat and simmer for 20 minutes. Dissolve arrowroot in water, stir into soup until it thickens slightly. Add remaining ingredients, stir well. Garnish with additional onion. Serve immediately.

PEASANT VEGETABLE SOUP

3 leeks, thinly sliced
1 bunch bok choy, chopped
3 tablespoons oil or butter
8 cups water
1 lb. sliced zuchinni
    or 1-10 oz. package frozen
1/4 cup amaranth or quinoa (opt.)
1 cup asparagus pieces
1 cup peas
1 cup spinach, chopped
  salt to taste

Saute leeks and bok choy in oil. Add the water, bay leaf, amaranth, and cook covered over low heat for 20 minutes or until the amaranth is done. Add the remaining ingredients and simmer 5 minutes longer. If not using amaranth, reduce cooking time to 10 minutes.

Add any additional vegetables to this soup. Flavor improves with age.
CROCK POT: Throw in all but the last 3 items, let cook several hours until tender (overnight is fine). Add the remaining ingredients, cook until tender.

MINESTRONE

1/4 lb. dry beans (see page 7)
Boiling water
2 quarts water
4 tablespoons leeks, chopped
2 tablespoons olive oil
1/2 lb. zucchini, peeled and diced
1/4 lb. string beans, cut in small pieces
3 cups boy choy or cauliflower, cut small
1 shallot, crushed
Salt and basil to taste

Pour boiling water over beans and let stand 2 hours. Drain and then cook in 2 quarts of water for 4 hours. Saute leeks and zucchini in olive oil for 5 minutes. Add to the beans. Add string beans, bok choy or cauliflower, shallot and salt and basil. Cover and cook over a low heat 1-1/4 hours. Serve.

ONION SOUP

3 tablespoons butter
3 cups chopped onion
2 tablespoons flour (see p. 159)
6 cups water
1 bay leaf
salt to taste

Saute onion in butter or oil until brown. Blend in flour, gradually stir in water. Add bay leaf and salt if desired and cook over low heat for 30 minutes. Discard the bay leaf. Serve hot. If desired any cooked seafood may be added during the last 2 minutes of cooking.

SEAFOOD BOUILLON

2 lbs. fish trimmings
2 quarts water
1 bay leaf
1/2 cube butter
2 carrots, sliced
3 stalks celery, chopped
1 large onion, sliced
pinch thyme
3 sprigs parsley
2 teaspoons salt

Combine and boil together for 1 hour; strain. This makes a good basic stock. It can be made a week ahead and kept in a covered jar in the refrigerator.

Notes:

SPINACH SOUP

4 cups water
2 bunches spinach, chopped
2 tablespoons oil
1/2 cup leeks, thinly sliced
1/2 cup ground nuts
1 teaspoon curry powder, (or to taste)
1 cup cooked beans (optional)
Salt to taste

Bring water to boil. Add spinach and simmer for 5 to 7 minutes. Saute leeks in oil and add to the spinach. Add ground nuts, curry powder and cooked beans if desired. Stir well and heat thoroughly, it's ready to serve!

ZUCCHINI SOUP

3 lbs. zucchini, cut into chunks   Yield: 6 portions
1/4 lb. lean ham, chopped
3-1/2 cups water
1 teaspoon salt (opt)
1/4 teaspoon pepper
1/2 cup chives or leeks, chopped

Combine all ingredients and cook for 1 hour or until zucchini is tender. Put in a blender and blend well for a 'creamy' soup, if desired. Reheat and serve.

84

TURKEY VEGETABLE SOUP

2 lbs. Turkey (apprx. 2 legs)
3 medium carrots, sliced
2 stalks celery with tops, sliced
2 teaspoons salt
1/4 teaspoon pepper
1/2 teaspoon dried basil leaves
2-1/2 quarts water
1 cup onion, coarsely chopped
1/2 tablespoon oil
Parsley, chopped

Rinse turkey and place in a 6-quart kettle. Add 2 cups water and simmer 2 hours, or until tender. Remove from stock, take meat off bone, chop into small pieces, put back into the pot. Saute onion until brown. Add with remaining ingredients, bring to boil, reduce heat and simmer at least 1 additional hour.

Also see crock pot cookery, p. 148.

NOTES

AVOCADO MOUSSE

2 tablespoons unflavored gelatin in
1/2 cup cold water (see thickeners p.159)
1/2 cup boiling water
3 cups avocado, mashed
  (aprox. 5 very ripe avocados)
2 tablespoons parsley, minced

1/2 teaspoon celery powder
1 teaspoon salt
1/2 cup dressing
Dash of Tabasco to taste
  watercress

Soak gelatin in cold water for 5 minutes. Add boiling water to completely dissolve. Combine with remaining ingredients in blender, mix well.
Pour the mixture in an oiled quart mold. Chill until firm.
Serve mold on a bed of watercress or any green leafy vegetable.

ORIENTAL SPINACH SALAD

2-8 oz. bunches of spinach
1/4 cup oil
1/4 cup dilute vit C (see p. 153)
1 oz. mashed anchovy
1/2 lb. small shrimp, canned or fresh

Chop spinach, steam, then rinse in ice cold water. Combine with remaining ingredients. Toss well. Chill and sprinkle with toasted sesame seeds before serving.

CRAB & AVOCADO SALAD

Yield: 6 portions   Preheat Oven: 400°

1/2 lb. crabmeat
1/3 cup celery, chopped
3 hard boiled eggs, chopped (optional)
2 tablespoons pimiento, chopped
1 tablespoon onion, chopped
1/2 teaspoon salt
1/2 cup salad dressing
3 large avocados, whole
lemon juice
salt to taste
3 tablespoons finely chopped nuts
1 teaspoon butter, melted
2 tablespoons almonds, slivered

Mix crabmeat, celery, eggs, pimiento, onion, salt and salad dressing together.
Cut unpeeled avocados lengthwise in half. Remove pits. Brush halves with lemon
juice and spinkle lightly with salt. Fill avocados with crabmeat mixture. Toss
nuts and butter together and spoon over crabmeat filled avocados. Sprinkle with
almonds. Place in a baking dish and broil in a 400° oven for 5 minutes, or
until browned on top.

Wonderful un-cooked, also.

BEAN SPROUT SALAD

1 quart (1/2 lb.) mung bean sprouts
3 green onions, cut 1/2" diagonally
4 red radishes, thinly sliced
1/2 daikon radish, thinly sliced
1/3 cucumber, unpeeled, thinly sliced
    (on the diagonal)
1/2 lb. green beans, sliced (on the diagonal)

Rinse bean sprouts. Blanch in boiling water for 3 minutes, pour into colander & immediately dip into large pan of ice water to stop the cooking process.

Stir gently . When cool, remove colander from water and let drain. Turn onto double thickness of paper toweling and drain **thoroughly.**

Mix remaining ingredients with sprouts and then chill. Toss with salad dressing, p.67 & 68.

SPINACH SALAD

1 tablespoon chives, chopped
2 tablespoons leeks, diced
1/2 cup olives, chopped
Dressing of your choice
1 bunch, or 1 lb. spinach, fresh

Wash and chill fresh spinach. Mince chives, leeks and olives together until very fine and pulpy. Add dressing (see recipes p. 67, 68) and let stand to develop flavors. Tear spinach into small pieces. Toss with dressing and serve.

SESAME CUCUMBER SALAD

2 cucumbers
1/2 teaspoon salt
1/2 cup dressing
1/4 cup toasted sesame seeds
2 tablespoons minced chives

Peel cucumbers and slice very thinly.

Toss with remaining ingredients and chill.

Serve on a bed of mixed greens.

FISH SALAD

1 lb. firm white fish
Basic salad dressing
1/4 cup onion, chopped
1 Sliced cucumber
1 clove minced garlic
1 cup cut-up string beans
1 cup cooked beans
Sliced radishes
1 teaspoon herbs
Sea salt to taste

Poach, drain and chill fish. Cut fish into bite-sized cubes and marinate in the dressing of the day combined with the other ingredients.

Searve as an appetizer, salad or main dish.

GALA SALAD

1 head leaf or bib lettuce
6 carrots, chopped
4 celery stalks, chopped
1 jicama*, peeled and chopped
3 jalapeno chiles, sliced
1 cup of sprouts

Arrange lettuce leaves and place on a platter. Mound remaining ingredients on top of the lettuce, alternating colors. Drizzle Green goddess dressing over all.

*Jicama (hee'kah'mah): Is a very crisp juicy vegetable. Shaped like a turnip and the skin looks like a potato. Does not darken when cut. It's called the "Poor man's water chestnut" since it stays crisp even when stir-fried. Serve it raw, in salads or with dips. Add to soups, stir-fry or stews. Refrigerate after peeling. Usually available November to June.

HEARTY SALAD

1/3 cup carrots, cooked and finely diced
1/4 cup celery, diced
1/4 cup green pepper, diced
1/2 cup red onion, chopped (optional)
2 tablespoons parsley, minced
2-1/2 cups rice, cooked (substitutions: quinoa, millet, chopped nuts or seeds)
4 tablespoons cold pressed vegetable oil
3 tablespoons lemon juice
  pinch of thyme
  Sea salt to taste

Garnishes: almonds, sunflower seeds, cooked seafood or chopped nuts

Cook carrots until barely tender, dice finely and combine in a large bowl with celery, green pepper, onion and parsley.

Add rice or millet, if not tolerated substitute chopped nuts or seeds, and mix together well.

In a separate bowl combine oil, lemon juice, thyme and salt to taste. Pour over the salad. Toss thoroughly. Chill for several hours.

Garnish as your heart desires--have fun.

MOLDED SEAFOOD SALAD

1 tablespoon unflavored gelatin
1/2 cup cold water
1/4 cup boiling water
3/4 cups basic salad dressing (p.67)
1/2 cup diced celery
2 tablespoons green olives, chopped
1/2 green pepper, minced
1/2 teaspoon salt
1-1/2 cups seafood, cooked
2 tablespoons pimentos, chopped

Soak gelatin in cold water to soften, dissolve in hot water. Mix with dressing, combine with the remaining ingredients.
Pour in mold and chill intil firm.

RUSSIAN SALAD I

3 artichoke bottoms
watercress
shrimp
celery, diced

anchovies
parsley, chopped
oil
vinegar

sardines, diced
crab, flaked
caviar
celery salt

Place three artichoke bottoms on a bed of watercress. Fill one with shrimp and diced celery, mixed with oil and vinegar dressing. Fill one with rolled anchovies sprinkled with chopped parsley. Fill one with diced sardines, crab flakes, and caviar. Serve with oil and celery salt. This very fancy version makes a lovely first course for a dinner party or buffet.

RUSSIAN SALAD II

1 Bunch spinach
1 zucchini, sliced
1 cauliflower, cut-up
1 cauliflower whole

asparagus spears
green onions
green peas, raw
Basic Dressing

Line a bowl with spinach leaves. Cook the vegetables "al dente", barely tender, by steaming them quickly. Chill them until crisp and place mounds of sliced zucchini, cauliflower chunks, asparagus spears, green onions and peas around a small head of cauliflower in the center. Serve with the basic dressing. Almost any combination of vegetables can be used.

SHRIMP SALAD WITH LEMON-DILL DRESSING

3 cups rice, hot, cooked*
1/4 cup oil
1/3 cup lemon juice
1 clove garlic, minced
1 teaspoon dill weed
1/4 teaspoon salt
1/4 teaspoon tarragon
1/8 teaspoon paprika
3/4 lb shrimp, cooked
2 tomatoes, cut into wedges
3/4 cup celery, sliced
1/3 cup parsley, chopped

*Too soon for starch? Substitute sprouts, vegetables or mung bean noodles, broken into small pieces.

When you can tolerate some carbohydrates, add cooked whole, quinoa, amaranth, brown rice, millet or buckwheat groats.

Toss vegetables (or rice or millet) together with oil, lemon juice, garlic, dill weed, salt, tarragon and paprika. Cover and chill several hours.
Just before serving add shrimp, tomatoes, celery and parsley. Toss lightly.

TABOULY SALAD

3 cups sprouts
1 cup parsley, minced
1/2 cup onion, minced
2 ripe tomatoes, chopped
2 teaspoons dried mint or basil
   (or 1/4 cup fresh herbs)
2 lemons, juiced
1/4 cup olive oil
garlic powder
pepper to taste

Mix all ingredients together and season to taste with garlic powder and pepper.
Onion and tomatoes are optional if they are not tolerated in your diet.
Let sit for 1/2 hour or more to blend flavors. Serve on lettuce leaves.

Tabouly variations: The addition of most any chopped or sliced vegetable go
goes well in this flavorful salad. Some possibilities are celery, green pepper,
avocado and mushrooms. A protein rich salad can be made by adding sunflower
seeds, chopped almonds or sunflower seed sprouts.

NUTTY STUFFED TOMATOES

3/4 cup nuts (or seeds) chopped
6 large tomatoes
1 teaspoon salt
1 cup parsley, chopped
1/2 cup green onions, sliced
1/4 cup mint, fresh, chopped
1/4 cup vegetable oil
1/4 cup lemon juice
1/4 teaspoon pepper
lettuce leaves
lemon wedges

Core tomatoes, cut slice off of stem ends, reserving slices. Scoop out center over bowl, (save pulp) leaving a firm shell. Sprinkle on insides with 1/2 teaspoon salt; invert on paper toweling for 30 minutes to drain.

Chop tomato pulp coarsely, add to nuts, parsley, green onion, mint, vegetable oil, lemon juice, remaining 1/2 teaspoon of salt and pepper (if desired), and toss gently.

To assemble, spoon nut mixture into tomato shells, mounding slightly. Top each tomato with reserved tomato slice, garnish with sprigs of mint if desired. Arrange on lettuce lined salad platter. Garnish with lemon wedges.

TURKEY SALAD

1 cup turkey, cooked, diced
2 cups rice, chilled*
1 cup celery, diced
1 medium green pepper, shredded
2 tablespoons pimiento, chopped
2 tablespoons parsley, chopped
1/2 cup sunflower oil (or olive oil)
1/3 cup lemon juice
1/2 teaspoon curry

*Too soon for starch? Substitute sprouts, chopped nuts, vegetables or mung bean noodles, broken into small pieces. When you can tolerate some carbohydrates, add cooked whole, quinoa, amaranth, brown rice, millet or buckwheat groats.

Mix turkey, rice, celery, green peper, pimiento and parsley together and chill.

Combine oil, lemon juice and curry.

Let mixture stand for 1 hour, pour over salad just before serving.

TOFUNA

1/2 pound tofu
1 can tuna
1/4 cup tahini
1 green onion, chopped
1 small cucumber, diced
1 clove garlic, crushed
   (or 1 tsp garlic powder)

Drain tofu and tuna, mix thoroughly.

Use as filler for stuffed tomatoes, peppers, etc; sandwich spread, cracker topping, vegetable dip, "crepes".

NOTES

NOTES

HURRY-UP HEARTY HASH

1/2 cup celery, chopped
1/2 cup nuts, chopped
1 egg or egg subs. (p.158)
2 tablespoons oil
1/2 teaspoon salt
1 clove garlic, pressed
2 cups potatoes, cooked, grated or
            beans, cooked, mashed

Combine all ingredients.
Shape into patties.
Brown both sides in lightly oiled skillet.

Great for a breakfast change!

This recipe is another FAVORITE, because
it's so versatile, AND it travels nicely.

103

FALAFEL

2 cups dry garbanzo beans
1/2 cup cold water
1 tablespoon safflower oil
1 clove garlic (to taste)
2 tablespoons parsley
1/4 teaspoon cayenne
1 cup minced green onion

Soak garbanzo beans overnight and drain. Finely grind garbanzos in food
processor, adding water as needed until blended into a smooth paste.
If using a blender, grind 1/2 cup at a time.

Add chopped garlic, minced parsley, and cayenne. Mix well.
Shape into 1" balls. Place on greased baking pan. Cover with foil. Bake at 350°
covered for 15 minutes. Turn. Bake uncovered 10 minutes.
In a hurry? Spread 1/2" thick on greased cookie sheet. Bake covered 15 minutes.
Uncovered 15 minutes and cut into squares.

Garnish with green onions and serve with tahini (sesame butter) or other sauce.
Serve an an appetizer, a snack, in pita bread.

DELICIOUS: Crumble and use as a coating for sauteed tofu, fish or chicken.

SUNFLOWER SEED WEDGE

1 cup carrots, grated
1 cup celery, chopped
1 teaspoon onion, minced (optional)
1/2 teaspoon salt

1 teaspoon basil
1 cup sunflower or almond butter
1/4 cup sunflower seeds, toasted

Combine all but sunflower seeds and pat into an 8" pie plate.
Refrigerate until ready to serve.
Cut into wedges for serving and sprinkle toasted sunflower seeds.

VEGGIE NUT LOAF

1 cup carrots, grated
1 cup tomatoes, diced
1 cup celery, grated
1/2 cup green pepper, grated

2 tablespoons oil of the day
1 clove garlic, minced (optional)
1 cup ground nuts or seeds of your
   choice. Salt to taste

Combine all ingredients and mold into an oiled serving dish.
Top with sprouts, chill and slice.
NOTE:
Both of these loaves are great for sack lunches and traveling. They keep well
and flavor improves on standing, so double the recipe and save one for later.
For best results, prepare the day before serving.

SUNFLOWER-CARROT CASSEROLE

Yield: 8 portions   Preheat Oven: 300°

1 lb. ground turkey or rabbit
1/2 cup onion, chopped
1/2 cup celery, chopped
1 clove garlic, minced
4 cups carrots or parsnips, thickly sliced
3 cups tomatoes
1/2 teaspoon salt
1 cup whole millet or quinoa (optional)*
1/2 cup sunflower seeds or chopped almonds

*If starch is not tolerated in your diet, increase sunflower seeds or almonds to
   1 & 1/2 cups.
Brown meat with onion, celery and garlic. Combine with remaining ingredients in
   large baking dish.
Sprinkle a few chopped nuts or seeds on top.
Bake at 300° for 1 hour with millet or quinoa; only 1/2 hour without.
Note: Instead of baking, this casserole may also be prepared by simmering   over
   over a low heat in a heavy pan with a tight cover for 45 minutes.

NUT LOAF

1/2 cup Brazil nuts
1 cup almonds
1 cup sunflower seeds
1/4 cup flax seed, ground
1/4 cup water
2 small onions, diced (optional)
1/2 cup parsley, fresh
1/2 teaspoon sage
1/2 teaspoon thyme
1/2 teaspoon salt
1/2 teaspoon sweet basil

SAUCE:
1/2 cup almonds, ground
2 cups water
1 tsp seasoning, see above.
2 tablespoons arrowroot flour
Dash of cayenne pepper
2 tablespoons oil
1/2 teaspoon salt

Grind nuts and seeds in a processor, blender or grinder.
Combine remaining dry ingredients, mix well. Add the water, mix again.
Place in a well oiled loaf pan and bake for 25 minutes at 350°.

Sauce: Combine all ingredients, mix well in small saucepan, bring to boil,
(stir constantly) reduce heat, simmer over low heat until thick. Pour over
cooked loaf. Serve hot.

NOTE: This loaf is a great traveler, good hot or cold, with or without the
sauce. Make a double batch, keeps well in frig. Freeze for a busy day.

PONSET

1/2 lb. mung bean noodles (bean threads)
1 red onion, chopped
2 cloves garlic, chopped
2 cups celery, sliced
1 cup green pepper, sliced
1 cup cooked, cubed, turkey (sub any cooked poultry or meat)

*Sprouts or rice noodles may be substituted.
Soak noodles in very hot water. (Do not cook) Set aside.
Saute onion in oil or small amount of water.
Add garlic, celery and green pepper and saute until vegetables are tender-
    crisp.
Add meat and seasonings to taste.
Toss with drained noodles and serve hot.

NOTE: This simple, VERY TASTY, dish is one of the "stars" in my cooking classes

NOTES

MEAT ROASTING TEMPERATURES AND TIMES

In roasting meats season with salt and pepper, place fat side up on a rack in an open pan. Insert meat thermometer, if desired, in center of meat. Do not add water and do not cover. Remember that roasted meat continues to cook after it has been removed from the oven.

Roast meats at a constant temperature of 325° unless otherwise indicated.

	Approximate Weight (Pounds)	Internal Temperature on Removal from oven	Approximate Cooking Time In Hours
Beef			
Standing Rib	4 to 6	140°(rare)	2-1/4
		160°(medium)	2-1/2
		170°(well done)	3
Standing Rib	6 to 8	140°(rare)	2-1/2
		160°(medium)	3
		170°(well done)	3-1/2

	WEIGHT	TIME	
Rolled Rib	5 to 7	140° (rare)	3-1/4
		160° (medium)	3
		170° (well done)	4-1/2
Sirloin Tip	3-1/2 to 4	150° to 170°	2-1/4
Tenderloin whole (425°)	4 to 6	140° (rare)	45 minutes
Tenderloin half (425°)	2 to 3	140° (rare)	45 minutes

Veal

Leg	5 to 8	170°	3
Loin	4 to 6	170°	2-1/12
Rolled Shoulder	4 to 6	170°	3

Fresh Pork (325° to 350°)

	WEIGHT	TIME	
Loin, center	3 to 5	170°	2
Loin, half	5 to 7	170°	3-1/2
Leg (fresh ham)	10 to 16	170°	4-1/2 to 6
Leg, half (fresh ham)	5 to 8	170°	3-1/2 to 4

Lamb

Leg, whole	5 to 9	140° (rare)	2-1/4 to 3
		160° (medium)	2-1/2 to 3
		170° (well done)	3 to 3-1/2
Leg, half	3 to 4	175° to 180°	2 to 2-1/2
Rolled shoulder	3 to 5	175° to 180°	2-1/2 to 3

See crock pot cooking page 149 for ideas in preparing less tender cuts of meat.

OLD FASHIONED POT ROAST

Yield: 10 portions   Preheat Oven: 450^0

3 lbs. (aprox.) lean brisket of beef
1 large chopped onion (or 1/2 cup dry, minced)
1 small bay leaf
1/2 teaspoon salt
1/2 teaspoon black pepper, coarsely ground
1 clove garlic, minced

Rub garlic and pepper on meat, place in a greased Dutch oven or heavy saucepan.
Brown for 10 minutes on each side in a pre-heated, very hot oven, (450^{0}F.).
Slowly and carefully add 1 cup water and remaining ingredients.
Reduce oven temp to 300^{0}F.
Cover and bake about 3 hours or until tender.

After browning, cleaned, cut-up root vegetables (see page 7) may be placed on
top of the roast for a simple one-dish-meal.

Or one hour before done, add 2 cups hot water and 1/2 cup brown rice or millet
or quinoa, cover and continue to bake at 300^{0}F.

Throw some squash or baking potatoes in the oven to bake along with the roast.
Conserve oven heat and get out of the kitchen

WAISTLINE BEEF PATTIES

1 teaspoon mustard, powdered
1 lb. ground beef, lean **
1 cup onion, fresh, finely diced
     OR 2 teaspoons dry, minced onion
1/2 teaspoon salt
1/4 teaspoon black pepper
1/8 teaspoon garlic powder

Mix mustard with 1 tablespoon warm water; let stand 10 minutes for flavor to develop.

Combine mustard with remaining ingredients; mix well, but do not overmix.

Shape into 6 patties. Broil to desired doneness.

**OPTIONAL: ground chicken, turkey, pork or lamb (add pinch of dried oregano to the lamb).

NOTES:

VEAL A LA MODE

2 lbs. shoulder of veal, cut into 2" cubes
2 lbs. tomatoes, cleaned, peeled and diced
1 small bay leaf
1/2 teaspoon salt
1/2 teaspoon ground thyme
1 clove garlic, chopped, or 1/4 tsp. garlic powder
1/16 teaspoon ground black pepper
1 lb. potatoes (4 small), peeled, cubed (optional)
1 lb. cut green beans* (frozen maybe used)

*Use any variety of fresh or frozen vegetables.

Sprinkle spices and garlic on meat, then brown in a heavy saucepan.
Add tomatoes & bay leaf.
Cover and simmer over low heat 1 hour or until meat is almost tender.
Add potatoes and cook 20 minutes longer.
Add beans (or vegetables) and continue cooking until meat and vegetables
are tender.

Add a GALA SALAD (page 92) for delightful meal.

ROASTING POULTRY

All kinds of poultry including chicken, turkey, duck and goose are delicious roasted. Poultry can be roasted whole, either stuffed or unstuffed.

Whole onions, chopped celery, an apple, and various other vegetables may be used instead of the traditional bread or starchy stuffing. They add flavor and moisture to the roasted bird.

Simply sprinkle with seasonings of your choice, (poultry seasoning, garlic, onion powder) insert a few vegetables and bake.

Plan the roasting time for a large bird so it will be done 20 to 30 minutes before you plan to serve it. It will be easier to carve after it has been allowed to stand for a few minutes.

The meat of the fleshy part of the drumstick feels soft when a bird is done. Or, you can tell if it is thoroughly cooked if the drumstick moves up and down easily, and the leg joint gives easily or breaks.

A meat thermometer is your best bet with whole turkeys. To test for doneness place the thermometer in the inner thigh muscle of the turkey. When it reads 180° to 185°, your turkey is done.

POULTRY ROASTING GUIDE

	Ready-to-cook Weight	Approximate Total Roasting Time at 325°
	Pounds	Hours
Chickens:		
Whole	2-4	1 to 2
	5 to 8	2-1/2 to 3
Ducks	4 to 6	2 to 3
Geese	6 to 8	3 to 3-1/2
Turkeys: whole	6 to 8	3
	8 to 12	3-1/2 to 4
	12 to 16	4-1/2 to 5
	16 to 20	5-1/2 to 6
	20 to 24	6-1/2 to 7
Parts & pieces	3 to 8	2-1/2 to 3
Boneless turkey roasts	3 to 10	3 to 4

See slow, crock pot cooking p. 140

ALMOND RABBIT

Yield: 6 portions   Preheat Oven: 375°

1/2 cup potato flour (sub. arrowroot or tapioca)
1 teaspoon salt
1/8 teaspoon pepper
1 teaspoon paprika
1 rabbit, cut-up, approx. 2-1/2 lbs.
2 tablespoons potato starch
6 tablespoons water
1 cup almonds, finely chopped
2 tablespoons almond or sunflower oil
salt as desired, to taste

Mix potato flour(or substitute), salt, pepper and paprika together.

Coat cut up rabbit pieces with flour mixture.

Combine potato starch and the water and dip the rabbit pieces, then coat them
    with the finely chopped almonds and place in pan.

Drizzle oil over rabbit pieces and sprinkle with additional salt to taste if
    desired.
Bake at 375° for 30 minutes. Turn and then bake an additional 40 minutes
until well browned.

LEMON BROILED CHICKEN

1/4 cup lemon juice
1 teaspoon grated lemon peel
1 teaspoon salad oil
1/2 teaspoon salt
1/2 teaspoon ground ginger
1/2 teaspoon paprika
1/4 teaspoon instant onion powder
1/4 teaspoon ground black pepper
2-1/2 lbs. broiler-fryer chicken, quartered

In a small bowl, combine lemon juice and peel, oil, ginger, paprika, onion powder and pepper; mix well. Brush over chicken. Place chicken in broiler pan, skin side down. Broil 7 to 9 inches from heat source for 10 minutes. Turn chicken and continue broiling, turning and basting until browned and crisp, about 25 minutes longer.

CHICKEN AND BROCCOLI BAKE

Yield: 6 portions   Preheat Oven: 375°

2 lbs. fresh, cut-up steamed broccoli
    or 2- 10 oz. packages frozen broccoli
4 tablespoons thickener
2 cups chicken broth
1 lb. cooked chicken, sliced **
1/2 cup chopped nuts
2 tablespoons butter, melted

Preheat oven to 375°. Cook broccoli until just tender.
        Do not overcook! Mix thickener and cold chicken broth in a shaker,
so that it does not lump. Simmer, stirring constantly, over a medium heat until
thickened and smooth. Season to taste.

Place broccoli pieces in a baking dish and cover with chicken. Pour gravy
mixture over the chicken and broccoli. Combine chopped nuts and melted butter
and sprinkle on top. Bake uncovered 20 to 25 minutes until bubbly and browned.

**Turkey or rabbit may be substituted for chicken.

SESAME CHICKEN

Yield: 6 portions   Preheat Oven: 375^0

1/2 cup arrowroot flour
1 teaspoon salt
1/8 teaspoon pepper
1 teaspoon paprika
1 chicken, cut-up
2 tablespoons arrowroot
6 tablespoons water
1 cup sesame seeds
2 tablespoons sesame or soy oil
   salt as desired, to taste

Combine first 4 ingredients in a bag, shake to mix; add chicken, shake again.

Mix arrowroot and water, dip chicken into mixture and then coat with the sesame
        seeds.
Place in pan, drizzle oil over chicken pieces and sprinkle with additional salt
        if desired.
Bake at 375^0 for 30 minutes. Turn and then bake an additional 40
        minutes longer until well browned.

CHICKEN STROGANOFF

2 tablespoons vegetable oil
1 lb. chicken, chopped or ground
1 medium onion, chopped (optional)
1 clove garlic, minced or pressed (optional)
1 cup chicken broth
1 teaspoon salt
1/4 teaspoon pepper
1/2 teaspoon thyme
  parsley, chopped

Heat oil in a wide frying pan over medium to high heat. Lightly brown chicken, just as chicken begins to brown add onion and garlic, stirring until limp.

Add broth, salt, pepper and thyme and simmer, (and stir) until thickened.

Serve over bean sprouts, bean threads, quinoa, rice or millet.

Garnish with fresh chopped parsley.

CURRIED TURKEY THIGHS

Yield: 6 portions

3 turkey thighs
1 teaspoon salt
1/2 teaspoon pepper
1 to 2 tablespoons oil
3/4 teaspoon curry powder
1/4 teaspoon powdered ginger
1-1/2 cups water
3 chicken bouillon cubes, crumbled
1-1/2 tablespoons arrowroot
1 teaspoon lemon juice

Season thighs with salt and pepper. In a heavy skillet, brown meat slowly on both sides using just enough oil to prevent sticking. Add curry powder and ginger and saute slowly for 5 minutes. Stir in water and bouillon cubes. Cover and simmer 1-3/4 hours or until turkey is tender. Remove turkey and keep warm. Skim off and discard any fat from juices. Blend arrowroot with 2 tablespoons of cold water. Stir into liquid remaining in pan. Cook, stirring until sauce boils and thickens slightly. Stir in the lemon juice. Serve turkey with thickened pan juices on the side.

EASY slow-cooker method:
Place all but the arrowroot and lemon in the pot. Cook overnight or all day, until tender. Follow above directions starting with "skim off fat".

SUMMER GARDEN TURKEY

Yield: 8 portions   Preheat Oven: 325°

1 turkey hindquarter roast (3 to 6 lbs.)
1/2 cup oil
2 tablespoons green onions, sliced
2 garlic cloves, pressed
1/2 teaspoon oregano
1/2 teaspoon basil
1/2 teaspoon tarragon
Salt and pepper to taste
2 cups vegetables, lightly steamed

Place turkey on a rack in a shallow roasting pan.

Combine all but the vegetables, baste the turkey on all sides.
Roast in a preheated oven for 2 to 3 hours, depending on the size of the roast.
When done a meat thermometer registers 180° to 185°. Baste the turkey
occasionally while baking.

Stir the remaining basting mixture into the vegetables (any variety you prefer).

Arrange vegetables on a platter around the turkey and serve.

NOTE: May be cooked in a "crock pot", see page 123

MEXICAN STYLE TURKEY

5 lbs. turkey breast, split
2/3 cup sunflower oil
1/2 cup lemon juice
3 cloves garlic, crushed (optional)
1/2 teaspoon salt
1/4 teaspoon coarsely ground black pepper
8 oz. tomato sauce (see p. 65)
Diced jalapeno peppers (to taste)
1 teaspoon garlic salt (optional)
1/2 teaspoon ground cumin

Place turkey in a shallow pan. Combine all ingredients and pour over the turkey to marinate.
Cover and refrigerate overnight, or least 8 hours. Turn occasionally.

Pour off marinade and use to baste turkey during roasting.

Roast turkey in a preheated 325^0 oven for 3 hours or until meat thermometer reaches an internal temperature of 180^0 to 185^0.

NOTE: May be cooked in a "crock pot", see page 123

KOREAN BROILED STEAK (KUN KOKI)   Yield: 6 portions

1 flank steak or chuck steak (2 lbs.)
3 tablespoons sesame seeds
1/4 cup sesame oil
1/2 teaspoon salt
2 cloves garlic, crushed
1/2 teaspoon black pepper
1/2 teaspoon ginger
1/4 cup apple juice
2 green onions, sliced

Score steak and place in glass dish or double plastic bags.
Combine all ingredients pour over meat and marinate overnight.
Broil steak about 3 minutes per side on preheated grill or under broiler.

TIPS FOR MARINATING:

Use double plastic bags instead of a shallow dish so you don't have to keep
turning and basting. When closing the bag, force the air out of it so the liquid
covers the food an all sides. Fasten shut with twist tie and place in a bowl in
case the bags leak.

This bag-it method saves fuss, requires only half as much marinade as an open-
dish method and is ready to travel to a picnic or barbeque.

FISH TYPES AND THE BEST WAY TO COOK THEM

COD has a mild flavor and firm, white flesh. Prepare it by any of the basic cookery methods. It goes well with a variety of sauces.

FLOUNDER and SOLE have delicate flavors, flaky white meat and a moist, fine texture. Try them prepared in any of the basic methods.

OCEAN PERCH is a red-skinned fish with a flavor similar to fresh water perch and bass. Lean, full-flavored ocean perch will go in almost any of your favorite dishes.

SALMON. the five best known species of salmon vary in flesh color from almost white to characteristic bright red. Try them barbecued, poached, baked, broiled, steamed or served cold for salads.

CATFISH has fine texture and excellent flavor. Deep fried catfish served   with with hush puppies is a favorite, but try catfish in a chowder or baste it with sesame seeds and butter and grill over hot coals.

RAINBOW TROUT makes a delightful and quick to fix, special meal. Handy frozen forms as well as fresh trout can be pan-fried, baked or barbecued on the grill. It is also wonderful stuffed or poached.

RED SNAPPER with it's snowy white meat has a sweet flavor and faint pink cast. Fillets or steaks are particularly good broiled or baked. And, whole red snapper is delicious prepared with a stuffing.

HALIBUT is good baked or poached. Try halibut steaks basted with a sauce or marinade and then broiled or grilled.

COOKING HINTS

A QUICK GUIDE TO COOKING FISH

Timing is the real secret of delicious fish cookery. Here's a simple rule for timing the cooking of fish. Measure the fish fillet or steak at its thickest part, then figure 10 minutes of cooking time per inch of thickness for baking. If the fish measures less than 1", or another method is used, shorten the cooking time proportionately.

If the fish is frozen, increase the cooking time. If you are going to cook the fish in foil or in a sauce, allow an extra 5 minutes per inch. Your fish will be done when the flesh becomes opaque and flakes very easily. Insert a fork at the thickest part and twist to test done-ness.

TO BAKE: Place cleaned, dressed fish in a greased baking dish. Brush with butter, oil or sauce to keep it moist. Lemon and/or onion slices under and over the fish will add flavor and prevent sticking.
Bake at 350^0. Whole fish, fillets and steaks lend themselves well to baking.

TO BROIL: Select fillets, steaks.   Arrange in a single layer on a well greased broiler rack. Keep fish 4" from the heat.

Baste with melted fat or oil or marinade before, after and during broiling. Do not turn.

HELPFUL HINTS FOR BROILING AND BARBEQUEING:
  Salad dressings (see p.67, 68) are tasty marinades, simply brush on before, and/or during broiling.

TO BROIL OUTDOORS ON A GRILL, purchase a length of fiberglass window screening. Cut a piece to place on the grill, under the fish. Grease to prevent sticking. The small pieces of fish don't fall into the coals.

For whole fish, wrap screen completely around the fish, fasten with a turkey skewer so you can turn occasionally.

While others are barbequeing red meat, you can use the same coals and enjoy fish. This diet can almost be fun.

PAN OR OVEN FRY: Dip clean, dressed small fish or fish servings into water then into breadcrumbs, cornmeal or flour. (Pan Fry) Heat 1/4" oil in a pan. Place coated fish in a single layer in the hot oil. Turn once midway through the cooking.

OVEN FRY: Place fish in a well greased shallow baking dish. Pour a little melted butter or oil over the fish. Bake in a preheated 400° oven. Do not turn.

POACH: Place liquid to barely cover a single layer of fish in a shallow wide pan such as a frying pan. Nut milk, plain or seasoned broth or water, or wine are some of the liquids that can be used. Bring liquid to a boil. Add fish then reduce heat to low; simmer gently until done.

TO STEAM: Use a steam cooker pot with a tight cover, deep enough to hold a wire basket or rack. Pour about 2" of water into the pot and bring to a rapid boil.

Place fish on rack or basket, place in pot keeping fish above the water. Cover pot tightly and steam until done.

DO NOT OVER-COOK! See page 128 for cooking instructions.

FISH FILLETS ALMANDINE   Yield: 6 portions

1/4 cup butter or oil
3 tablespoons almonds, slivered
2 lbs. fish fillets (snapper, cod or sole)
1 tablespoon lemon juice
1/2 teaspoon garlic salt
1/4 teaspoon pepper

Heat 2 tablespoons of oil in a large skillet. Add almonds and cook over a
medium low heat 2 to 3 minutes until golden brown, stirring constantly. Remove
almonds and set aside.
In remaining oil, cook fish 3 to 4 minutes on each side until fish fillets flake
when pierced with a fork.
Remove to a warm platter. Stir lemon juice, garlic salt and pepper into pan
drippings with almonds and spoon over fish.

If you are rotating your foods, Vit. C., lime or pineapple juice may be substituted for lemon juice (see p. 153)

HERBED BAKED FISH STEAK

Yield: 4 portions
Preheat Oven: 425°

1-1/2 lbs. fresh halibut steak
1 teaspoon instant minced onion
1 teaspoon mustard, powdered
1/2 teaspoon oregano, leaves
1/4 teaspoon marjoram, leaves
1/2 teaspoon salt
1/16 teaspoon ground black pepper
4 teaspoons lemon juice
paprika

Wash fish and arrange in a baking dish. Combine minced onion, mustard, oregano, marjoram, pepper and lemon juice with 2 teaspoons of water; let stand 10 minutes for flavors to blend. Spoon evenly over fish.

Bake uncovered in a preheated hot oven (425°) 17 to 20 minutes or until fish flakes easily with a fork. Garnish with paprika. Serve with lemon wedges if desired.

BAKED STUFFED FISH

3 to 5 lbs. whole fish (bass, cod, bluefish, haddock, etc.)
1/4 cup oil
1/2 cup chicken broth
1/2 cup celery, finely chopped
1/2 cup onion, finely chopped
1-1/2 cups rice or millet, cooked (optional*)

Clean and dress fish.

Saute onion and celery in oil until lightly browned. Add quinoa, rice or millet*
and broth, mix well. Place in cavity of fish, not more than 2/3 full. Close the
opening with skewers or toothpicks laced together with string.
Put on an oiled oven proof platter or oiled paper or cooking parchment paper in
a shallow baking pan. Cut 3 or 4 gashes through the skin on each side to keep
the fish in shape during baking.
Bake at 400° for 30 to 45 minutes or until meat flakes easily with fork. To
serve, make a deep cut along the backbone, then cut in pieces at right angles to
the backbone.

* When you can tolerate some carbohydrates, use cooked whole, quinoa, amaranth,
brown rice, millet or buckwheat groats. Until then, substitute coarsely ground
nuts or seeds.

133

FILLET OF SEAFOOD IN ITALIAN SAUCE

Yield: 6 portions
Preheat Oven: 400^0

2 small onions, chopped
1 clove garlic, minced
2 tablespoons oil
8 oz. tomato sauce (see p. 65)
1- 8 oz. can water
1/4 cup parsley, chopped

3 tablespoons lemon juice
1-1/2 teaspoons salt
1/8 teaspoon pepper
1/2 teaspoon dried rosemary

2 lbs. fillet of sole (snapper or cod)

Saute onions and garlic in oil until onions are transparent. Add tomato sauce, water, parsley, lemon juice, salt, pepper, rosemary and honey and simmer about 1/2 hour.

For a quick 'n easy: at this point add chunks of fish to sauce,   simmer 10 minutes and serve.

For a dash of panache: Place 2 tablespoons of sauce in the middle of each fillet. Roll up jelly roll fashion. Place in shallow baking dish with the ends underneath to keep them from unrolling. Pour remaining sauce over the fish rolls. Bake at 400^0 for 25 minutes.

MAHI-MAHI LYONNAISE

Yield: 6 portions
Preheat Oven: 350°

2 lbs. Mahi-Mahi fillets*
4 cups onion, thinly sliced (optional)
1/4 cup oil
2 tablespoons lemon juice
2 tablespoons parsley, chopped
1 teaspoon dill weed, crushed

*Any firm fleshed fish may be used.

Skin fillets and cut into serving sized pieces. Cook onion in oil until lightly browned.
Place 1/3 of onion in bottom of a well greased baking dish, (12 x 8 x 2").
Arrange fish over onion. Sprinkle lemon juice on fish. Add parsley and dill weed to remaining onion and spread over fish.
Bake at 350° about 30 minutes or until fish flakes easily.

STUFFED TURBOT

Preheat Oven: 350°

4 flat pieces of turbot*
1/2 lb. crab meat
1/4 cup Basic Salad Dressing (p. 67)
1 teaspoon Grey Poupon Mustard (optional)
1/4 teaspoon salt

*Any thin boneless fillet may be substituted.

Mix the crab with dressing and mustard (salt, if desired). Place equal amounts on each piece of turbot. Roll up the pieces and fasten with toothpicks. Arrange in a glass dish in which they will fit rather snugly, sprinkle lightly with paprika. Bake at 350°for 20 minutes.

TUNA CASSEROLE

Preheat Oven: 350°

1/2 stick butter or oil
1 leek, (or onion) minced
2 tablespoons flour (see p. 159)

1-1/2 cups clam juice
4 cups chopped vegetables
2- 7oz. cans tuna

Saute leek in butter or oil. Gradually work in the flour to make a smooth mixture. Add clam juice gradually and stir until thick. Place vegetables and tune in a casserole dish, and pour sauce over all. Garnish with chopped nuts, or seeds if desired. Bake at 350° for 20 minutes.

BASIC PRAWNS

Wonderful as an appetizer or main dish.

1-2 lbs. prawns, uncooked, in shell
1 quart water
1 lemon, sliced or
      2 tablespoons lemon juice
1 small onion, sliced (optional)
2 teaspoons pickling spice (optional)

Defrost prawns if frozen, rinse and drain. Combine the other ingredients in a large kettle and bring mixture to boil.
Add prawns, reduce to low heat, cover for 5 minutes. Remove shrimp, drain and cool. Remove shells and de-vein (remove the black strip on their backs) .

Serve chilled as an appetizer with a cocktail sauce for dipping, or marinate and serve as a salad or appetizer, or use in recipes calling for cooked prawns or shrimp.

BROILED SHELLFISH

1 lb. scallops or 1 pint oysters
1/4 cup oil or melted butter
1 tablespoon lemon juice
1/4 teaspoon salt
1/4 teaspoon paprika
chopped parsley

Defrost scallops or oysters if frozen. Rinse and drain.
Arrange shellfish over bottom of a heat-proof dish. Combine oil, lemon juice,
salt and paprika. Spoon half of mixture over shellfish.
Broil 3 inches away from heat for 8 to 10 minutes. Baste occasionally with
remaining mixture. Garnish with chopped parsley and serve.

Notes:

BOUILLABAISSE   (Fish Stew)

2 lbs. fish
1 quart water
1/2 cup oil
2 onions, chopped
1 clove garlic, crushed
thyme
bay leaf
fennel

8 mussels
8 clams
1 cup lobster meat
1 cup shrimp, shelled
1/2 cup pimentos, sliced
tiny pinch of saffron

Clean fish, simmer in the water for 10 minutes. Remove fish, continue to boil water until reduced by half. Save the broth. Cut the fish into serving sized pieces.

Place the oil in a heavy soup pan. Saute' onions & garlic, add spices, and broth, and boil for 5 minutes. Reduce heat, add everything except the saffron. Simmer another 10 minutes. Crumble saffron into soup and stir gently.
Serve with fresh homemade crackers, (see page 161-162).

139

HEARTY ALASKA COD CHOWDER

Yield: 6 portions

1-2 lbs. Alaska cod fillets*
1 cup onion, chopped
1 cup zucchini, chopped
1 large clove garlic, minced
1/4 cup oil
1 lb. cut-up tomatoes

2 cups tomato juice (see p. 65)
1/3 cup water
3/4 teaspoon salt
3/4 teaspoon crushed basil leaves
dash hot pepper sauce (optional)

*Any firm fish may be substituted.

Cut fish into large chunks.
Saute onion, zucchini and garlic in oil. Add remaining ingredients and heat to boiling.
Add cod and simmer, covered about 10 minutes or until fish flakes easily when tested with a fork. This recipe may be halved or doubled.

Microwave Method: Cut cod into large chunks. Combine onion, zucchini, garlic and oil in 3-1/2 quart microwave dish. Microwave, covered on High for 4 minutes or until onion is tender. Add tomatoes, tomato juice and seasonings. Microwave, covered on High 4 minutes or until boiling. Add cod. Microwave, covered, on High 4 minutes. Stir and microwave, covered, on High 2 to 4 minutes longer or until cod flakes easily when tested with a fork.

CLAM CASSEROLE

2 lbs. steaming clams
2 large leeks, thinly sliced
1 shallot, crushed
1/2 cup chives, minced
3 tablespoons oil
1 cup quinoa or amaranth seed
1-1/2 cup water
chives, chopped

Scrub the clams clean of all sand and wash them thoroughly in cold water several times.
In a heavy pan (dutch oven) saute leeks, shallot and 1/2 cup of chives in oil.
Stir in amaranth seed. Add water and clams. Cover tightly and cook over medium heat until the amaranth seed is cooked, about 20 minutes.
Season to taste. Garnish with additional chives and serve.

Notes:

NEW ORLEANS GUMBO

1/2 lb. shrimp
1 quart water
1 tablespoon oil
1 small onion, minced
1 clove garlic, minced
1 stalk celery, chopped
1 bay leaf

2 sprigs parsley, chopped
1/2 teaspoon thyme
1/2 cup amaranth*
1 tablespoon thickener
1/4 cup water
1/2 pint oysters
1 teaspoon file powder

Shell the shrimp, boil the shells 10 minutes. Discard the shells and add water to the broth to make 1 quart.
Brown vegetables in oil and add with spices to the stock. Stir in amaranth * if tolerated & 2 cups of water. Simmer 1/2 hour.
If you can't tolerate amaranth, use thickener (see p. 159), mixed with 1/4 cup of water. Simmer about 15 minutes.
Add oysters and shrimp and cook gently until the oysters begin to curl. Add file powder just before serving.

* When you can tolerate some carbohydrates, add quinoa, amaranth, brown rice, millet or buckwheat groats. If not, use bean sprouts, bean noodles or more vegetables.

FILLET OF FISH WITH SHRIMP SAUCE

1 bay leaf
1 clove
1/8 teaspoon thyme
salt to taste
4 fish fillets

1 tablespoon thickener (p.159)
2 tablespoons butter
1-1/2 cups clam juice
1/2 lb. small shrimp
paprika

Add 2" of water to skillet,, bring to boil, add spices, then reduce heat.
Add fish, poach for 5 minutes or until it flakes with a fork.
Mix thickener and butter to make a roux, thin with the clam juice.
Add the shrimp.
Pour over the fish, sprinkle with paprika and slide under the broiler to brown before serving.

Notes:

SEAFOOD RAGOUT

2 lbs. thick fish fillets
2 cups onions, sliced (optional)
2 cups carrot strips
2 tablespoons oil
1/4 cup thickener *
1 lb. tomatoes, diced

1 cup water
2 teaspoons salt (opt)
6 whole peppercorns
   or 1/8 teaspoon pepper
1 bay leaf
1 tablespoon lemon juice
   parsley (optional)

Cut fish into 1-1/2 to 2" chunks.
Saute' onions in oil until tender but not brown. Stir in thickener.
Add water, stirring constantly, then add tomatoes, salt, pepper and bay leaf.
Simmer 10 minutes. add fish, cover and continue to simmer 10 minutes more, or
      until fish flakes easily.
Sprinkle with lemon juice and parsley before serving.

*Rice, millet or potato flour may be used, or see p. 159.

SAUTEED SCALLOPS

1 lb. scallops
2 cups water
2 tablespoons flour (see page 159)
3 tablespoons water
2 tablespoons chopped chives
3 tablespoons butter or oil
  salt, if desired

Flour very lightly. Melt the butter and add the scallops a few at a time, browning carefully on all sides.
Add water, chives and salt all at once. Stir gently with a wooden spoon until heated through. Serve at once.

NEAPOLITAN ZUCCHINI is a nice colorful accompanyment, add a salad, some home-made crackers for a simple, elegant meal.

SCALLOPS ST. JACQUES

1 lb. scallops
3 TBSP. thickener (see p. 159)
1/4 cup butter or oil
3 tablespoons water
2 tablespoons chives, minced
salt to taste

Wash scallops. If large cut into small pieces. If small leave whole.
Simmer in water until tender, about 3 minutes. Remove with slotted spoon.
Set aside. Boil the water rapidly until reduced almost by half. Add leeks and
   chives and simmer in the liquid 10 minutes.
Make a roux of the flour and butter/oil. Stir and gradually add the liquid. Salt
   to taste. When sauce is creamy stir in the scallops.
Place in baking shells. Top with chopped nuts, dot with butter and slide under
   the broiler until nicely browned. See TASTY TOPPINGS, page 72.

Notes:

SHELLFISH COCKTAIL

1 lbs. cooked crab, shrimp, lobster or oysters
3/4 cups ketchup (see recipe p. 69)
1 tablespoon lemon juice
1 teaspoon horseradish
1/4 teaspoon salt
Tabasco (optional)
Lemon wedges
Parsley

Wash and drain shellfish, defrost if frozen.

Arrange in cocktail glasses.

Combine remaining ingredients except for lemon wedges and parsley and spoon over the shellfish.

Serve chilled with lemon wedges and parsley as garnish if desired.

SLOW (CROCK POT) COOKING

Get out of the Kitchen, and still "cook from scratch" by slow cooking in an "unwatched pot". Just plug it in and let it cook all day or overnight without stirring or fussing with it.

Breakfast can be a snap by starting it before bedtime. Grains, quinoa and amaranth can cook all night and be ready to eat on rising.

Place a turkey hindquarter, pot roast, stewing hen, rabbit or whatever, in the pot at 10 p.m. and have tender, juicy meal ready at 6 a.m. After breakfast, place vegetables in the pot, on top of the meat, and let simmer until lunch or dinner time. Enjoy throughout the day.

Start dinner before leaving the house in the morning and come home to a hot wholesome, ready-to-eat meal in the afternoon.
Old Fashioned Bean Soup, Chili or Split Pea Soup, hot and ready to eat at any time of the day or night, are care-free, nourishing treats.

See SOUP RECIPES, pages 77 - 85. The majority of the cooked MAIN DISHES can be prepared in this simple slow-cook method without oils, fats or frying. SAUCES are a snap to prepare (applesauce, apple butter, tomato sauce, etc.). Just scrub, cut-up and place in the pot, let cook for a day or two, or until done..

Read the booklet that comes with the pot for additional ideas and time saving hints.

THE FOLLOWING SECTION CONTAINS SOME RECIPES THAT ARE HIGH IN CARBOHYDRATES,
USE ONLY WHEN YOU CAN TOLERATE SOME STARCHES

NUT, BEAN, and ROOT VEGETABLE flours (also called "meals" and "starches") are recommended instead of grains at first, for grains tend to be "allergenic", meaning they may cause allergic reactions.

Keep a food diary so you will be able to determine if your symptoms are allergic reactions, or Candida symptoms caused from eating too many carbohydrates.

149

COOKING BEANS

BASIC DIRECTIONS: Rinse, sort and search for stones. Reduce cooking time by soaking overnight. Cover with water by several inches.

QUICK SOAK: Bring to boil, let stand 2 hours, continue cooking.

Pressure cookers speed cooking time with beans, dried peas or lentils. Add water as needed during cooking, don't salt until almost done. Ratio of water to beans should be 3:1 (3 cups of water to 1 cup of beans).

After soaking, bring to boil, reduce heat and simmer for a long, long time, as long as possible; twice as long as the directions call for in order to avoid gas and indigestion; all day is not too long. A tablespoon of vinegar added at the beginning of cooking makes calcium more available, more easily absorbed and also prevents gas.

Use crockpot cooking for the simplest, hassle-free cooking of beans.

Cook 4 times the amount you'll eat and freeze them for use later. They thaw easily and make wonderful bean dips, refried beans, hummus, burritos and salads. (See recipes).
Add a hamhock at the start of cooking if desired. When beans are tender, remove the bone, cut off meat and mince and add back to the pot along with chopped onions, celery, chopped greens and spices of your choice.

COOKING WHOLE GRAINS

General Directions:

Rinse in cold water to remove dust, dirt and talc. Use brown rice and whole grains and seeds, since nutritional value and fiber are lost in hulling and polishing.

Water to grain ration is usually 2:1 (2 cups water to 1 cup grain). Rub a small amount of oil inside the pot to avoid sticking.

Add grain to cold water, bring to boil, turn down to simmer, cover and cook for: 20 to 30 minutes for groats, millet, amaranth, quinoa and barley; 45 minutes for rice or rye; Cook until bubbling stops and a slight crackling begins. To test for done-ness, spoon out a sampling, rinse with cold water and chew. Try to avoid peeking into the pot so that the steam won't escape.

When using a pressure cooker, follow manufacturer's directions.
Salt maybe added before (preferrably) or after cooking.
Refer to crockpot cooking for the simplest preparation of grains and beans.

Notes!

ALTERNATIVES TO WHEAT

Amaranth, buckwheat, kamut, spelt, teff, quinoa (pronounced keenwa), are delightful alternatives to wheat. Buckwheat, quinoa and amaranth are not related to wheat, and are essentially gluten-free. Kamut, spelt and teff contain gluten and are close cousins to wheat. These **super grains** are usually organically grown, which means pesticide-free and generally more nutritious than grains grown commercially with chemical fertilizers. Enjoy in a wide variety of forms, including whole grains, flour, and even pastas.

According to Marge Jones*, 1/2 cup of cooked grain ranges from 28 grams of carbohydrate for buckwheat - to 41 grams for teff or spelt. Amaranth and quinoa contain 35 grams. These high-fiber whole grains are complex carbohydrates, and are generally better tolerated by those with Candida yeast overgrowth than wheat and/or overly processed refined sugars and starches. Additional carbohydrate listings pp18-34.

These rich, hearty flours are heavier than wheat and take a little getting used to. See my Guide Book #6: *Allergy-Free Baking Tips,* for tricks of the trade.

Shop for these grains in Natural Food Stores, or by mail from: Allergy Resources, 1- (800) USE FLAX. *Super Foods* * by Marge Jones, a 36 page recipe and resource booklet: 2615 N. Fourth St. #616 Coeur d'Alene ID., 83814. $5.95, includes shipping.

SUBSTITUTIONS

BREADINGS AND COATINGS for Baked or **Fried Foods

REPLACE 'bread or cracker crumbs' with your own home made cracker crumbs, recipes on page 161.

GRIND any nut or seed into a meal. Sesame seeds are wonderful for liver or chicken, just moisten the food with water and dredge in the meal. Also try dry, minced onion; amaranth, quinoa or potato flours; dry, or shredded coconut. Bake or fry foods as usual. Use your imagination, write and let me know what you discover. I'll print your ideas in my monthly newsletter, ALLERGY ALERT.

**Frying with fats and oils is the least desireable way to prepare food. You can bake, poach, steam, simmer, even stir-fry with little or no added fats or oils.

This cookbook is to help you through the 'crisis' of starving out the candida yeast, while avoiding highly allergenic foods at the same time. It's purpose is not to teach basic nutrition . . . that will come later when you're feeling well enough to care.

SUBSTITUTIONS

HOW IN THE WORLD CAN WE LIVE WITHOUT SLICED BREAD??

"FINGER FOODS" don't have to be be placed between 2 slices of bread.
Lots of foods can be rolled, stacked, filled, dipped or stuffed to make a
"sandwich". See the recipes beginning on page 161 for making your own crackers,
muffins, waffles, flat breads, nutri-ola bars or pancakes from grains, beans,
nuts, seeds or amaranth. Also see BROWN BAG ideas on page 46.

If tolerated in your diet: corn chips, potato chips, rye krisp, rice crackers or
pan cakes.

PASTA SUBSTITUTIONS

Vegetables may be stuffed and used as finger foods, salads' or main meals. Try
red or green peppers, avocados, scooped out zucchini, acorn squash shells, baked
potatoes, artichokes, tomatoes, cucumber 'boats'.
The only limits are your imagination and foods you may be allergic to.

VINEGAR SUBSTITUTES
All vinegars contain mold because they are produced by a fermentation process.
Since we need to avoid molds, here are some substitutions: lemon juice, lime
juice, unsweetened cranberry juice or dilute vitamin C (ascorbic acid)
1 teaspoon in 1/4 cup of water.

FLOUR SUBSTITUTIONS

1 Cup of White Flour = 1/2 cup arrowroot or tapioca with 1/2 cup of
                       another flour or nut meal (see nut butters).

                     = 7/8 cup buckwheat, quinoa or amaranth flour

                     = 3/4 cup cornstarch or 7/8 cup corn flour

                     = 5/8 cup potato flour or 3/4 cup potato starch.

                     = 3/4 cup oat flour or 1-1/2 cups rolled oats (ground).

                     = 3/4 cup rice, soy, barley, millet, or bean flours.

Flours can be made from any starchy vegetable, legume or grain.
Legume (bean) Flours are very hard, which makes them difficult to grind. Use a
coffe or seed grinder for best results. Process according to manufacturer's
directions. Process into a fine powder.
Try soaking beans overnight in water, then finely grind into a "mush". Decrease
the amount of liquid used in the recipe to compensate for the water that has
soaked into the beans.

SUBSTITUTIONS, Flours and thickeners

Starchy Vegetable Flours can be made from squash, pumpkins, yams, potatoes, carrots, parsnips, etc. Clean thoroughly, peel and cut into small chunks, dry in a food dehydrator or a very slow oven, 200°F. several hours or over-night. Turn occasionally for even drying. Grind into a fine powder. Label and store in an airtight container.

A MEAL is ground up nuts or seeds, and may be substituted for any flour. A starch (arrowroot, tapioca, any flour) may need to be added to prevent crumbling and to improve the texture. Use the same grinding directions as given for Legume (bean) Flours.

"Alternative" flours are usually coarser than the wheat flours we are used to cooking with, and usually require more liquid than the original recipe calls for. Prepare recipe several hours in advance, let mixture stand for several hours or overnight for a lighter, more desireable finished product. Add baking powder to the batter just before cooking.
STARCHY VEGETABLES may be cooked, mashed or pureed for thickening stews, gravies or soups.

To avoid lumps when thickening liquids, dissolve in a small amount of cold water first, then add slowly, stirring constantly.

HELPFUL HINTS: Equivalents, Measures and Substitutions

Pound Equivalents

2 cups water
2 cups butter
2 cups chopped meat
4 cups all-purpose flour
1-7/8 cups rice
2-1/3 cups dried beans
2-2/3 cups ground oatmeal
6 cups rolled oats

Cooking Measures

60 drops	1 teaspoon
3 teaspoons	1 tablespoon
1 tablespoon	1/2 fluid ounce
16 tablespoons	1 cup
1 cup	8 fluid ounces
2 cups	1 pint
2 pints	1 quart
1/2 cup butter	4 ounces

Substitutes

1 tablespoon corn starch (for thickening)= 2 tablespoons wheat flour

See page 155 also for additional substitutions.

1 egg =	{1 tablespoon ground flax or psyllium seed mixed with
	3 tablespoons of water
1 egg =	2 tablespoons of apricot mixture (see recipe below)
1 egg =	2 tablespoons water + 2 teaspoons baking powder

APRICOT MIXTURE/EGG REPLACER

Place in bowl: 1 cup dried apricots. Cover with boiling water, let stand until soft. Puree in blender or processor. Cover, store in refrigerator.

EGG WHITE REPLACER

1 tablespoon plain unflavored gelatin
Dissolve gelatin in 1 tablespoon of water. Whip; chill, and whip again.

ENER-G Egg Replacer: by Ener-G Foods. Box 24724, Seattle, Wa. 981214.

Hint from JO's Kitchen: mix with liquid and let stand 10 minutes before using for best results).

Notes:

THICKENERS & BINDERS (wheat substitutes)

HOT SAUCES: gravies, white sauce, marinades, and so on, (need to be cooked:) Corn Starch, Potato Starch, Tapioca, Arrowroot, Agar (seaweed), Bean Flours. See pages 155, 156 also.

COLD: plain unflavored gelatin, from animal sources, ie. Knox Gelatin. Agar-agar (seaweed).

HOT OR COLD: (no cooking required) guar gum, pectin, gum arabic, xanthan gum*, locust bean gum. Substitute for flour or eggs when cooking with seeds, nuts and starches that crumble or fall apart when baked.

*XANTHAN GUM: is fun to play with in the kitchen. A small amount added to any liquid turns it into a creamy smooth 'mouthfeel' like rich ice cream. Meat or fish drippings (au jus) turn into fluffy sauces and gravies; fruit juice transforms into gelatin; nut milk and carob powder becomes like chocolate pudding; salad dressings thicken so they don't separate. Stays creamy after thawing, doesn't curdle.

Does not mix well by hand, a rotary mixer, blender or food processor is necessary for excellent results. Xanthan gum is also excellent as a substitute for gluten in breads.
ORDER: from Ener-G Foods (makers of Jolly Joan Egg Replacer and other hypoallergenic foods) Box 24724, Seattle, Washington 98124.

LEAVENINGS

Leavenings cause baked goods to 'rise' by trapping air bubbles in the batter (or dough). The bubbles are   acid and alkaline substances combining and creating a 'foam'. Yeast is usually not permitted on the candida diet because so many Candida hosts (like you) are allergic to it.

BAKING POWDER #1

1 part potassium bicarbonate
2 parts cream of tartar
2 parts any starch (arrowroot, rice flour, etc.)
Mix thoroughly and store in a covered container. Keeps well.

Baking Powder #2

1 teaspoon cream of tartar
1/2 teaspoon baking soda

Baking Powder #3

1/4 teaspoon baking soda
1/2 teaspoon any acid [lemon or lime
        juice, or powdered vitamin C
        (ascorbic acid)]

Add to liquid just before baking. Equals 1 teaspoon of baking powder.
Good formula for breads or muffins. Use immediately.
#2 and #3 do not keep well.

CRACKERS & PIE CRUSTS FROM FLOUR

2 cups amaranth or legume flour**
1 teaspoon baking powder or soda
1 teaspoon salt
1/3 cup oil or fat
1/3 cup cold water (approximate measure)

Combine flour, baking powder or soda and salt. After mixing well, add oil or fat and mix with a fork until crumbly. Add water slowly, as needed, form into 2 balls. Chill thoroughly.

CRACKERS   Preheat Oven: 350^0

Place ball on lightly greased baking sheet, roll out to about 1/4" thick. Dust dough with flour if necessary to keep from sticking to rolling pin. cut into 2" squares. Prick with fork all over. Bake in middle of preheated oven 350^0 for 10 minutes or until brown. (Time varies depending on type of flour used.) Watch carefully to prevent burning.

Optional: Sprinkle with chopped nuts, seeds or coconut and roll again before cutting into squares.

The formula for figuring carbohydrate content is on Page 15.

**See page 155 for flour choices.

PIE CRUST: Roll out chilled dough and arrange in pie pan, or press into place with fingers. Flute edge if desired. For pre-cooked fillings: prick with fork. Bake at 350^0 for approximately 15 minutes, cool and add filling. Chill & serve. GET CREATIVE Add singly or in combinations: 1 teaspoon dried herbs or spices, 1/2 cup coconut, 1/2 cup finely chopped nuts or seeds.

CUT FUN SHAPES with cookie cutters, make diamonds, stripes, hearts, circles or whatever.
SAVE CRUMBS from broken and odd-shapes, crumble and use for cracker or bread crumbs, for croutons, stuffings and so on.

CRACKERS AND PIE CRUSTS FROM NUTS AND SEEDS   Low Carbohydrate

2 cups meal (nut or seed)   1 teaspoon salt (optional)
1 teaspoon baking powder or soda   1/3 cup thickener*

Grind nuts or seeds in food processor or blender and combine with dry ingredients. Oil is usually not needed for crackers or crusts made with nuts or seeds.

*Egg replacer, ground flax or psyllium seed; xanthan gum or guar gum, arrowroot, tapioca or other flours. (See page 155)
Mixing and baking directions are the same as for crackers and pie crusts above.

NUTRI OLA
Breakfast Cereal -- Snack Bar -- Cookie

Pre-heat oven to 250°F.
Yield: 6 cups

2 cups nuts, grains or seeds, finely ground
1 cup nuts, grains or seeds, coarsely ground
1 cup nuts, grains or seeds, whole
1 cup dried fruit, chopped
1/2 cup sweetener

1/2 cup oil
2 teaspoons vanilla

Grind nuts and/or seeds in a blender and or food processor to desired consistency. Place sweetener, oil, and vanilla in a small bowl, mix well. Put remaining ingredients into a large bowl, pour liquids over the dry mixture and stir lightly.

Spread mixture in a lightly oiled baking pan (15 x 10 x 1"). Bake for 1 hour stirring every 15 minutes. Cool. Break into small pieces for cereal or large chunks for snacks. Store in labeled container.

NUTRI OLA SNACK BARS

In addition to the above add 2 beaten eggs (or egg substitute, see pages 158-159. Slowly add additional liquid (water, nut milk or juice) to make a stiff batter. Spread in pan as above; bake 20 minutes and do not stir. Cut into squares.

SUBSTITUTIONS for bread include:
PANCAKES, FLATBREADS, TORTILLAS, CREPES, POCKET (PITA) BREADS, WAFFLES ..

These are staple foods of people all over the world. The basic ingredients are some type of starch or flour and a liquid. Optional ingredients are eggs, leavenings (yeast, baking powder or baking soda) sweeteners, nuts, seeds, fruit, and all types of seasonings.

In other words 'anything goes', depending only on your taste buds and ethnic background. How it's cooked and shaped and seasoned depends on whether it will be used for breakfast, lunch, dinner, or dessert. The typical Western staple is a large, fluffy loaf that needs to be sliced so that we can toast it, spread it or stack it into a sandwich or finger foods.

When we can no longer eat the grains that are needed for this 'fluffy' type that requires slicing what do we do? Cry? Pout? Do without? No, we simply make "flat" breads. We don't need to slice, for we already have flat 'slices' to spread fillings on. We can roll them like jelly rolls, or we can stack them with all sorts of fillings in between, just like regular sandwiches.

Choose a basic pancake recipe and make it with the ingredients you are allowed to have in your menu plan . . . arrowroot, amaranth, potato, bean, nut or seed meal . . . experiment until you get it just to your liking . . . not too thick or thin . . . and then play with the fillings. (See page 48)

GET CREATIVE! You are limited only by your imagination and old ideas about what what one "should" eat at certain times of the day.

BASIC MUFFINS

Yield: 12 muffins
Preheat Oven: 400^0

1-1/2 cups amaranth or quinoa flour or nut meal
1/2 cup arrowroot or tapioca flour
1 teaspoon baking powder
1/2 teaspoon salt (optional)
1 egg or substitute
1/3 cup oil
1 cup nut milk or substitute any liquid

Sift dry ingredients together. Mix wet ingredients together well. Combine wet with dry, stirring until just blended, do not over beat. Fill greased muffin cups 1/2 full. Bake in preheated 400^0 oven for 12 to 15 minutes.

VARIATIONS:
Apple Spice: add 1 cup chopped apple, + 2 teaspoons cinnamon and 1/2 teaspoon nutmeg. Gingerbread: add 1/2 teaspoon cinnamon or allspice and 1/2 teaspoon ginger.
Pumpkin Spice: add 1 cup cooked pumpkin in place of liquid, 1/2 teaspoon nutmeg, ginger and/or allspice.
Pineapple-nut: add 1 8 oz. can of drained, crushed pineapple, 1/2 cup of the juice in place of liquid, and a dash of nutmeg if desired.
Helpful hints: The smaller muffin tins work better for heavy flours, and insure a lighter end product. See page 156. Still too heavy? Lower oven temp to 350^0 and bake an additional 10 minutes.

BASIC FLOUR PANCAKES

1-1/2 cups any flour
1/4 teaspoon salt
1 tablespoon baking powder

1 egg (or substitute)
1-3/4 cups water or nut milk
1/8 cup oil

Sift dry ingredients and mix well. Combine egg, nut milk, oil, mix well and add to dry ingredients. Bake on preheated, non-stick griddle, turn when browned and bubbly.

BASIC FLOUR WAFFLES

1-1/2 cups any flour
1/4 teaspoon salt
1 tablespoon baking powder
1 egg (or substitute)

1-3/4 cups nut milk
1/4 cup oil
1 tablespoon honey (optional)

Combine dry ingredients , mix well. Combine egg, nut milk, oil and honey together, mix and add to dry ingredients. Bake in hot waffle iron (non-stick).

Note: If batter thickens, add small amounts of liquid as needed.
Double Recipes: Use extras like bread slices. Cool pancakes on wire rack so they don't stick together. Make multi-layered sandwiches.

(Also see pages 48, 156, & 164 for additional helpful hints)

BASIC NUT OR SEED PANCAKES
Low Carbohydrate

2 cups seed or nut meal
1 teaspoon baking powder or soda
1 teaspoon salt (optional)

1/3 cup flour or thickener
1/3 cup cold nut milk, or water
1 egg or substitute

Combine dry ingredients together and mix well. Combine nut milk and egg and blend together with dry ingredients, mixing gently. Bake on pre-heated, non-stick griddle.

BASIC NUT OR SEED WAFFFLES
Low Carbohydrate

2 cups nut or seed meal
1 teaspoon baking powder or soda
1 teaspoon salt, (optional)
1/3 cup flour or thickener

1/3 cup nut milk or water
1/4 cup oil
1 egg or substitute

Combine dry ingredients, mix well. Combine milk, oil and egg and blend gently with dry ingredients. mixing gently. Bake in hot waffle iron, non-stick.

Note helpful hints on page 166.
(Also see pages 48, 156, & 164 for additional ideas)

SESAME PANCAKES
From: Jo's Kitchen

1 cup sesame meal
2 teaspoons baking powder
1/2 cup arrowroot
1-1/2 tablespoons oil
2 tablespoons sweetener (optional)
1/2 cup water
2 tablespoons sesame seeds

In a bowl combine oil, water and honey. Mix well. Combine dry ingredients and seeds, add to wet ingredients. Stir gently, so not over-mix. Bake on lightly oiled teflon pan until brown. Batter will thicken, thin with more water to desired consistency.

(See pages 48, 156, & 164 for additional ideas)

Notes:

BEANCAKES/PANCAKES
From: Pauline Adams

1/4 cup flaxseed meal
3/4 cup water
1/2 cup bean flour

1/4 teaspoon salt (optional)
1/2 teaspoon soda
1/2 cup chopped nuts (optional)

Mix together flaxseed meal and water. Combine bean flour, salt, soda and chopped nuts. Mix with soaked flaxseed meal and let stand at least 10 minutes, until mixture thickens. Cook on a lightly oiled, non-stick surface for best results. When done, transfer to warm platter, and sprinkle with goat cheese (if allowed) or any other topping of preference and place in a warm oven until cheese melts.

MORE HELPFUL HINTS:
For a lighter 'cake', mix the night before, don't add soda until just before cooking. Bean and other heavy flours yield a finer finished product the longer they 'soak'. Freezing the batter further improves texture.

Note: Double or even triple this recipe, cool on wire rack, or place towels in between until cool so they won't stick together. Store in refrigerator or freezer for future use as sandwich material.

Add ground or chopped nuts or seeds for variety. Package as individual servings and freeze for lunches and travel.

NUT BUTTER COOKIES

Yield: 2-1/2 doz.
Preheat Oven: 350⁰

1 cup any nut butter
1/2 cup sweetener
1/4 cup oil
1/2 teaspoon vanilla (optional)
1/4 teaspoon salt (optional)
2 cups any flour or starch

Preheat oven to 350⁰. Mix nut butter, sweetener, flavoring, salt and oil together until smooth. Add flour a little at a time and mix well after each addition. (It's usually best to mix by hand, do not use a food processer when adding the flour).

Roll dough into balls, place on oiled cookie sheet, flatten with a fork. Bake for about 10 minutes, watch closely to avoid burning.
Or form into logs, roll in waxed paper. Chill, slice 1/2" thick and bake. Uncooked dough keeps well in refrigerator. Slice and bake as needed. Freezes nicely also.

Notes:

FROZEN CRANBERRY SALAD
From: Jo's Kitchen

2 cups cranberries, cooked*
1 cup pineapple, crushed, unsweetened, drained
1/2 cup yogurt, plain, unsweetened
1/2 cup sour cream
1/2 cup walnuts, finely chopped

Combine all ingredients and mix thoroughly. Place in a lightly greased 8" square pan or mold. Freeze overnight.
To serve, cut in squares or slices and arrange on crisp greens.

*To cook cranberries: Place one (1 lb.) package of cranberries in pan with 1 cup water. Bring to boil, simmer about 10 minutes, add honey, stir. Cool. Follow above directions.

DRIED FRUIT/SEED BARS

2 cups dried fruit, seedless
2 cups nut or seed meal

Mix and knead (very stiff). Press firmly into oiled pie pan or cookie sheet. Set aside for 24 hours. Cut in bars. Store in refrigerator.

PUMPKIN BREAD
From: Jo's Kitchen   Preheat Oven: 350⁰

1-1/2 cups rice flour
3/4 cups potato flour
1-1/2 teaspoons baking soda
1/2 tablespoons cinnamon
1/2 teaspoon salt
3/4 teaspoon nutmeg
3/4 teaspon cloves
1 teaspoon ginger
1 cup chopped dates

1 cup raisins
3/4 cup butter or oil
1-1/2 cup sweetener
1 cup pineapple juice
3 eggs or substitute
1-1/2 cups cooked pumpkin
1-1/2 teaspoons vanilla

Combine dry ingredients together and mix well. Combine wet ingredients together and mix well. Gradually and gently blend all ingredients together. Batter will be very thick.
Spread in lined pans and bake at 350⁰ for about 1 hour until a knife inserted in the middle comes out clean.

Delicious, high-carbohydrate treats, keep well- and are good travelers.

RUM BALLS

1/2 cup walnuts
3/4 cups currants
1/4 cup dried apricots
2 teaspoons rum or rum flavoring (or pineapple juice)

1/2 teaspoon vanilla
1/2 cup coconut, grated

Place nuts and fruits in a food processor or grinder and process until the fruit is chopped and the mixture clings together in a large ball. Add the rum and vanilla and process a few seconds more.
Form into small balls and roll in grated coconut or chopped nuts.

NUT BUTTER CAROB FUDGE

1 cupnut butter
1/4 cup carob powder

1/8 cup honey, or to taste
1/2 cup grated coconut or
            chopped nuts

Combine and form into balls. Roll in coconut. Chill. Or form into 1-1/2" logs. Roll in chopped nuts or coconut. Wrap in waxed paper or foil (shiny side next to food). Chill, slice.

HERE AT LAST!
A NEW GAME THAT MAKES ROTATION DIETS
EASY AND FUN!!

- Provides a SIMPLIFIED APPROACH to a complicated dietary concept.

- A color-coded SYSTEM to put some FUN back into the kitchen!

- MAKES THE FAMILY INDEPENDENT!

- Contents:

    Colorful, plastic coated master chart
    Food Diary instructions
    Guidelines, helpful hints
    Colorful visual aids, recipes
    Food family lists, Menus, Vegetarian Food
       Combining Chart & More.

YES, there's life after allergies! You can get well if you -
#1: ELIMINATE highly allergenic foods
#2: ROTATE all other foods for a while..
    NOT FOREVER, probably for less than a year. YOU WILL GET WELL !!

$15.95 plus $2 shipping. Send to P.O. Box 31065 Seattle, WA 98103

174

RECIPE BOOK DESIGNED TO ACCOMPANY
THE ROTATION GAME

- AUTOMATICALLY ROTATED FOR YOU
  Each colored section contains recipes carefully
  created for days 1, 2, 3, or 4. i.e. GREEN DAY?
  Open to the green section and start cooking.

- COLOR COORDINATED with the MASTER CHART of
  the ROTATION GAME.

TOTALLY FREE OF ALL GRAINS
(Barley, Buckwheat, Corn, Oats,
Millet, Rice, Rye & Wheat) AND
SOY, PEANUTS, MILK PRODUCTS,
EGGS, YEAST & REFINED SUGARS

P.O. Box 31065   Seattle, WA   98103   (206) 547-1814

175

NOW YOU CAN HAVE A NUTRITIONIST IN YOUR KITCHEN -

Sally Rockwell, recovered addict (food, drugs, and alcohol), ex-"junk-food-junkie", is now devoted to simplifying ALL special diets. Her interest in your well being, plus her love of good food has inspired her to create fun, easy "how-to" books, games and tapes so you can help yourself regain vitality.

Sally's audio and video tapes cover everything you wanted to know about allergies and candida yeast but didn't know who to ask. She takes your hand and leads you step-by-step through problem areas, smooths out menu planning, offers encouragement and support, gives tips and tricks on how to get family and friends to co-operate, **PEPS YOU UP and RENEWS YOUR ENTHUSIASM.**

FOOD ALLERGY RELIEF
CANDIDA CONTROL
SET of both tapes   (save $2)
VIDEO, What's Left To Eat?

Send $ 1⁰⁰
for sample
newsletter ☺

Sally
♡

Check first with your local book & health food stores - If not available, use this order form.

Coping with Candida Cookbook . . . . $ 10.95 . _____

Rotated Allergy Recipes . . . . 10.95 . _____

The Rotation Game . . . . 10.95 . _____

Food Allergy Relief Tape . . . . 10.95 . _____

Candida Control Tape . . . . 10.95 . _____

    Set of both audio tapes . . . . 19.95 . _____

Rotation Diet Video 60 min. (VHS) . . . . 29.95 . _____

Allergy Alert Newsletter (per year) . . . . 18.00 . _____

    Shipping: $3.00. For each additional item add $1.00 . . . . _____

      (Add'l shipping charges outside U.S.A.)

    WA State Residents add 8.2% sales tax . . . . _____

Free Shipping
with 4 or more items.

Send for **FREE** **Allergy Alert** *& info on other products and services*

Rush this order to:

Total $ _____ (US Funds)

Name_____

Address_____

City & State_____ Zip_____

Visa/MC# _____ Exp_____

Quantity Discounts available

Send check, money order or Visa/MC # to: Sally Rockwell P.O Box 31065 Seattle WA 98103 (206) 547-1814

NOTES

INDEX

ALLERGIES   6, 7, 39, 152

BAKED GOODS - CAUTION

Beancakes   169
Crackers &
  Pie Crusts (flour)   161
Crackers &
  Pie Crusts (nut/seed)   162
Fruit/Seed Bars   171
Fudge, Nut Butter   173
Muffins, Basic   165
Nutri Ola (granola)   163
Pancakes, Basic (flour)   167
Pancakes, Sesame   168
Rum Balls   173
Salad, Frozen Cranberry   171
Waffles (flour)   167

CANDIDA
Candida, What is it?   1
Carbohydrates, counting   15
Carbohydrates, Caution! High.   21
Cave Man Diet   9
Control, 4 Steps for   2
Dietary Guidelines   4

Don't Feed the Yeast   11
Foods to Avoid   17
Live it up Foods, Snacks   18
Master Chart   7
Questions & Answers   12

CARBOHYDRATE LISTINGS
All Foods   22-34
Counting   15
High Carbo Foods   21

CONDIMENTS
Seasoned Salt   72
Tasty Toppings   72

COOKING GUIDES
Beans, Basic - how to cook   150
Crock Pot Cooking   149
Fish Cooking Guide   129
Fish Types, Cooking Hints   127
Grain Cooking Guide   151
Measurements, Cooking   157
Meat Roasting Guide   110
Poultry Roasting Guide   117

FISH

Almandine	131
Baked, Herbed	132
Baked, Stuffed	133
Bouillabaisse	139
Chowder, Hearty Alaska	140
Clams & Amaranth	141
Crab Bisque	61
Gumbo, New Orleans	142
In Italian Sauce	134
Mahi Mahi Lyonnaise	135
Ponset	108
Boiled Prawns	137
Scallops, Sauteed	145
Scallops, St. Jacques	146
Seafood Ragout	144
Shellfish, Broiled	138
Shellfish, Cocktail	147
With Shrimp Sauce	143
Tuna Casserole	136
Turbot, Stuffed	136

HELPFUL HINTS

Amaranth	152
Breakfast Ideas	42
Cleaning Foods, How to	38
Diets, Ideal vs. Real	35
Dining Out	41
Dinner Ideas	44
Fast Food Eateries	36
Lunch Ideas	43
Lunches, Brown Bag	46
Sandwich Fillings	48
Social Occasions	40
Spreads and Dips	49
Sprouting Guide	52
Sprouting Sprouts, How to	51

MEAT

Beef Batties, Waistline	114
Rabbit, Almond	118
Pot Roast	113
Steak, Korean Broiled	126
Veal A La Mode	115

POULTRY

Chicken & Broccoli Bake	120
Lemon Broiled Chicken	119
Sesame Chicken	121
Stroganoff, Chicken	122
Turkey Ponset	108

INDEX, con't

Turkey, Curried Thighs	123
Turkey, Mexican	125
Turkey, Summer Garden	124

SALAD DRESSINGS

Basic	67
French	68
Green Goddess	67
Guacamole	68

SALADS

Avocado Mousse	87
Bean Sprout Salad	89
Chinese Salad	87
Crabmeat & Avocado	88
Fish Salad	91
Gala Salad	92
Hearty Salad	93
Russian I & II	95
Seafood	94
Sesame Cucumber	90
Shrimp with Lemon Dill	96
Spinach	90
Taboulie	97

Tofuna	100
Tomatoes, Stuffed	98
Turkey	99

SAUCES, SPREADS, BUTTERS

BBQ Sauce	69
Clam Sauce (or soup)	71
Gado Gado Sauce	70
Guacamole	68
Ketchup	69
Nut & Seed Butters, Spreads & Milk	73

SOUPS

Almond	75
Clam & Avocado Broth	75
Beet Borscht	76
Broccoli Soup	77
Garlic Soup	78
Hot & Sour Soup	79
Minestrone	81
Onion	82
Peasant Vegetable	80
Seafood Boullion	83
Spinach	84
Turkey Vegetable	85
Zucchini	84

SUBSTITUTIONS

Coatings for baked and fried	153
Eggs	158
Flours	155
Leavenings, baking powder	160
Measurements, cooking - subs.	157
Thickening agents, binders	159
Vinegar	153
Xanthan Gum	159

VEGETARIAN MENU 45
(Added in 1994)

VEGETABLES

Beans, Savory	55
Beansprout, Hot dish	62
Cauliflower, Blushed	56
Eggplant, Spiced	57
Green Beans & Burger	63
Lentils, Curried	54
Marinated Veg. Salad	58
Sesame Vegetables	61
Sophisticated Vegetables	60

Interested in Vegetarian or Vegan recipes and menu plans?
If so, send a note and we'll notify you when Sally's forth coming book,
Allergy-Free, Calcium-Rich & Vegan, is available.

Sally Rockwell P.O. Box 31065 Seattle, WA 98103

NOTES

CAN YEAST ALLERGY BE DRAINING YOUR VITALITY?

CANDIDA QUIZ*

Troubled By:

☐ Confusion, fatigue, depression, poor memory

☐ Digestive problems, constipation, bloating, diarrhea, gas, belly aches?

☐ PMS (premenstral tension syndrome), recurrent vaginitis, bladder infections or prostatitis?

☐ Crave sweets, breads, alcoholic beverages?

☐ Recurrent headaches or muscle and joint pains?

☐ Skin rashes, hives, psoriasis, eczema, itchy ears or rectum?

☐ Fungus infections like thrush, athlete's foot, jock rash?

☐ Taken antibiotic drugs, birth control pills, cortizone or steroids?

☐ Sensitive to tobacco, perfume, chemical odors or auto exhaust?

☐ Feel uncomfortable in moldy, damp rooms?

*"The Yeast Connection,"
Wm. Crook, M.D.

Score
1 point for each "YES" answer
3 to 4 — possibly,
5 to 8 — probably,
8 to 10 — almost certainly, yeast is contributing to your symptoms.

If, after a thorough examination, your physician says, "You're physically fine, the test results are within normal bounds" and you still experience these symptoms, then read **COPING WITH CANDIDA COOKBOOK**.

DIS-EASE IS OPTIONAL.
If you're ready to get well, try the **cave man**** diet for 10 days. If you feel worse for 3 or 4 days and then your symptoms disappear, you're on your way to good health.

**Check with your doctor before trying this or any other diet, this is information only and not to be taken as medical advise.